3.95

C000218797

Ameena's Rama

Sara Kabil and Abubakr El-banna

Ta-Ha Publishers Ltd.

Copyright © Ta-Ha Publishers Ltd. 1429 AH/2008 CE

First Published April 2008

Published by
Ta-Ha Publishers Ltd.
Unit 4, The Windsor Centre,
Windsor Grove,
London, SE27 9NT
Website: www.taha.co.uk
E-mail: sales@taha.co.uk

All rights reserved. No part of this publication may be reproduced, stored in any retrieval system or transmitted in any form or by any means, electronic, mechanical, photocopying, recording or otherwise without the prior written permission of the publishers.

Written by: Sara Kabil and Abubakr El-banna
General Editor: Dr. Abia Afsar-Siddiqui
Typeset and cover design by: Rebecca Monks

A catalogue record of this book is available from the British Library.

ISBN-10: 1 84200 089 6
ISBN-13: 978 1 84200 089 2

Printed and bound by: Mega Basim, Turkey

How to use this book

Ameena's Ramadan Diary is not a book in the traditional sense, although you can read it from start to finish and still find it very useful.

In order to get the most out of this book, we recommend that you start reading it prior to Ramadan and then use it and its tools as a guide before and during the Holy month.

As you read Ameena's daily entries, you will be directed to certain pages that are further ahead of where you are reading - jump quickly to see what has been referenced and then return to where you were reading and carry on.

There are some useful sheets such as the Ramadan Preparation Programme that we suggest you photocopy and follow as best you can. If you didn't already know and as you will soon discover, preparing for Ramadan is essential in making it a personal success.

There are lots of helpful tips and hints in the daily entries and useful articles and material in the second section of the book so try and implement them as best you can, but remember everybody is different and you can only do your best in your own personal way.

May Allah guide us all to a Ramadan that is full of reward in this life and the next (ameen).

16th Rajab - 6 weeks before the start of Ramadan

Monday - 6 weeks! 6 weeks to go until Ramadan! Are you kidding me? I couldn't believe it when Sabeena sent me an e-mail today about an event at the end of the week regarding the virtues of Ramadan - alhamdulillah for friends like her. I learnt so much last Ramadan but to say that I got the best out of it would be a massive exaggeration! In fact it would be a complete lie. When Ramadan was over last year, I made a promise to myself that the next Ramadan would be different, in a good way of course. So, this Friday, 7pm at the Town Hall: 'The virtues of Ramadan' - it's in the diary.

Wednesday - Has this week at work dragged on or what? Well at least tomorrow's Thursday, which isn't too bad. Must remember to call Aisha; we're supposed to meet up for coffee and a catch-up this weekend. We've been doing that every first weekend of the month since we graduated from uni! I wonder if she'll come to the event on Friday. I'll send her a text later.

I feel an urge to do so much this year in Ramadan - surely this is from Allah. I've been thinking about the event for the last couple of days now and I'm really taking it seriously. Earlier, I started writing down what I did last Ramadan so as to remind myself of the good things I did and the good things I said I was going to do and didn't. I've also written down a few questions to ask the sheikh – can't wait!

Sabeena's sister is about 8 days overdue. I've told her that if they have a baby girl they should definitely call her Ameena, but I think their hearts are set on Khadeejah. Well if they're not going to call her Ameena then I guess Khadeejah's ok.

 Write down all the positive things that you did last Ramadan as well as those areas that need improvement with the aim of maximising the benefits of this Ramadan, insha'Allah.

Friday – What an event! How could I know so little? There I was thinking I've got to do so much during the month of Ramadan to get it right this year and I didn't even realise that I have to do so much before it even starts. I'm just so glad I went alhamdulillah. We were given a handout called "The Ramadan preparation programme" (RPP) which is brilliant. It won't be easy sticking to it, but I'm going to try my best and I know if I do that then Allah will help me get what I want out of it.

And it didn't stop there – we went through the virtues of Ramadan according to the Prophet Muhammad's 轡 *khutbah* on the Holy month. The sheikh highlighted some key *ahadith* and *ayat* from the Qur'an about the month too – he more than covered everything. I really didn't feel that asking some of the questions I had written down were going to be of any benefit because they seemed so basic after he had finished. Sabeena didn't think twice about asking her questions though – she never shies away from anything that girl.

The sheikh also stressed on making *du'a* we physically make it to Ramadan. He was saying that so many people take the month for granted and don't realise its importance; some aren't fortunate enough to live to see it start.

He stressed how blessed and important this month is and that it was chosen by Allah for the Qur'an to be revealed in. He said that we must prepare for it from now if we really want to benefit from it. It's all about preparation! The best thing to do is to set goals, so I managed to scribble down my goals for Ramadan, which are:

1. To finish reading the Qur'an at least once
2. To concentrate on good manners, bettering my character, purifying my thoughts and intentions
3. To persevere and maintain the acts of worship that I decide to do, no matter how small
4. To spread the word, involve family, friends, etc.
5. To follow the RPP and Ramadan checklist as best as I can.

Khutbah: Islamic sermon or speech

Ahadith (plural of hadith): Narration of the sayings and deeds of the Prophet Muhammad ﷺ

Ayat (plural of ayah): Verses of the Qur'an

Du'a: Supplication to Allah

Turn to:
- **Page 56** for the Ramadan Preparation Programme (RPP)
- **Page 61** for the Prophet's ﷺ Khutbah on Ramadan

 Ayat and Ahadith

Abdullah ibn Umar reported that when the Prophet ﷺ sighted the moon of Rajab (two months before Ramadan) he used to pray to Allah in the following words:

اللهم بارك لنا فى رجب وشعبان وبلغنا رمضان

Allahumma barik lana fi Rajab wa Sha'ban wa ballighna Ramadan

O Allah! Make the months of Rajab and Sha'ban blessed for us, and let us reach the month of Ramadan [i.e. prolong our life up to Ramadan, so that we may benefit from its merits and blessings] (Bukhari, At-Tabarani and Ahmad)

23rd Rajab - 5 weeks before the start of Ramadan

Monday – 'Heart Focus' Week - Masha'Allah!!! Sabeena's sister gave birth today to a baby girl. Khadeejah arrived at about 6pm! I'll have to pop down to the High Street tomorrow and pick up a nice little outfit or maybe I'll just get her some vouchers.

There are still 5 weeks to go before the start of Ramadan and it seems a bit strange getting into serious 'Ramadan mode' this early, but alhamdulillah it's a good thing and I also have the RPP to thank for that. I've been through it about ten times now and this week is 'Heart Focus' week! Thinking about it, it's exactly what I need as I've been a bit lazy Islamically over the last couple of weeks. I feel as though I'm not concentrating in *salah* and other things as I should. I spoke to Aisha about that and she said she felt the same. Well at least 'Heart Focus' week will be a good first step. As the sheikh made very clear, we must start with tawbah, a real repentance called *tawbah nasooha*, where we intend to stop doing any of the sins we do and promise not to go back to them again. After I finish this entry I will sit down with myself for a few minutes and really think about my tawbah, be remorseful for my sins, ask Allah for forgiveness and hope never to repeat them again.

I think I'll go and do that now.

Turn to:
- **Page 63** for How to make Tawbah

Salah: Prayer, particularly the five daily obligatory prayers which are the second pillar of Islam

Tawbah nasooha: A real repentance, asking Allah's forgiveness for one's sins and intending never to repeat them again

Tuesday - I listened to a lecture about Heaven and the virtues of the 'good people' on my way home from work today. The programme said that listening to such lectures, as well as reading books, will help the heart get into the right state, so I've stocked up my car with all kinds of lectures and I plan to listen to the whole series before Ramadan comes around! It's better than listening to the radio. The sheikh was just going to start talking about what you get in heaven when you say 'La Hawla Wala Quwwata Illa Billah' but I'd already been parked up outside the house for five minutes and Mum had been staring at me from the window for four! I'll pick it up again in the morning on the way in to work tomorrow, insha'Allah.

I also started reading a book at bedtime about Patience and Gratitude. I had to force myself to put it down and go to sleep, it was so motivating.

La Hawla Wala Quwwata Illa Billah: There is no might and no power except with Allah

Thursday - What a hectic week it's been at work. I can't believe how I can be so in tune with the programme in the mornings and utterly distracted at work. I haven't had a second to spare during the day and I've been rushing through my prayers. I honestly need to start working on my *khushoo'.* I remember someone once told me that strengthening your faith will increase your khushoo'. It's a good thing I've started listening to those lectures and reading those books - maybe that will help; I'm already building my treasures in Jannah by saying '*La Hawla Wala Quwwata Illa Billah.*' I'll also try to do some *tasbeehs* and *istighfars* during the day.

Khushoo': Humbleness and submission of the heart and mind with concentration in worship

Tasbeeh: Glorifying or praising Allah such as saying *Allahu Akbar* (Allah is Great), *Alhamdulillah* (All praise to Allah), and *Subhanallah* (Glory to Allah)

Istighfar: Seeking forgiveness from Allah by saying *Astaghfirullah* (I seek forgiveness from Allah)

Turn to:
- **Page 83** for Dhikr and Remembrance of Allah

 Ayat and Ahadith

O ye who believe! Turn to Allah with sincere repentance [*tawbah nasooha*]: in the hope that your Lord will remove from you your ills and admit you to Gardens beneath which rivers flow…(Surah At-Tahrim 66: 8)

Abu Musa reported, "We were walking along with Allah's Apostle 🕊 on a journey when the people began to pronounce *Allahu Akbar* in a loud voice. Thereupon Allah's Messenger 🕊 said, 'O people, show mercy to yourselves for you are not calling One Who is deaf or absent. Verily, you are calling One Who is All-Hearing (and) near to you and is with you.' Abu Musa told that he had been behind him (the Holy Prophet 🕊) and reciting, 'There is no might and no power except with Allah.' He (the Holy Prophet 🕊), while addressing 'Abdullah ibn Qais, said, 'Should I not direct you to a treasure from amongst the treasures of Paradise?' I ('Abdullah ibn Qais) said, 'Allah's Messenger, do it, of course.' Thereupon he (the Holy Prophet 🕊) said, 'Then recite: There is no might and no power except with Allah.'" (Muslim)

30th Rajab / beginning of Sha'ban - 4 weeks before the start of Ramadan

Sunday - 'Fasting and Qur'an' Week - I woke up feeling awful on Saturday, which completely messed up my weekend. I ended up spending it all at home with a king-sized box of tissues and a dustbin next to my bed!

At least it got me thinking about how much Qur'an I have to catch up on. But before I get on to that, I need to make *qada* of my missed fasts from last Ramadan. Thinking about it now, I should have made them up straight after Eid last year. Not to worry, I have Sabeena to encourage me as she has a few days to make up too, so we've decided to start by trying to fast tomorrow (if I'm feeling better that is!). Should be ok, insha'Allah.

Now, back to reading Qur'an. It's got to be a major priority because Ramadan is the month that the Qur'an was revealed in after all. I'll have a chat with Sabeena about when and how much we should be reading.

Qada: The making up of fasts missed for a valid reason during the previous Ramadan

Turn to:
- **Page 85** for valid reasons for forgoing a fast

Tuesday - And I thought fasting again was going to be easy! Can't believe how tired I got. I think the hardest bit of all was not having that morning cup of coffee that I am definitely addicted to! It's a good thing I'm fasting now though; I definitely don't want to be feeling like this come Ramadan! I called Sabeena at around 2pm and she sounded even worse than me! Now she's a coffee addict! It was good to meet up with Sabeena for *iftar* after work and go through our checklist taken from the programme, although Sabeena didn't really say a word until she'd finished her meal and had dessert! We're going to start reading at least 3 pages from the Qur'an every day from now on. I'll have to dig out the one with the meaning of the words in the margins - at least that will help me concentrate more on my reading.

Fasting really is an amazing form of worship and I read that there is a special gate of Paradise called Ar-Raiyan for people who observe the fast to enter from on the Day of Judgement. I hope I'm from the ones who enter through that gate, insha'Allah.

Iftar: The evening meal for breaking the daily fast

Wednesday - I'm so glad I'm starting to get my act together and am somewhat following the programme. It really does make a difference if you have a plan to follow, and even though I admit I'm not the most organised of people, I'm trying to follow it as best I can. I'm planning to do a kind of Islamic shopping trip this weekend. I need to pick up a Qur'an with meanings for me and Sabeena from the Islamic bookstore in the mosque. I didn't find the one I had at home. I'm sure I'll find it in Irfan's room - he's the kind of brother who helps himself to my reading material. I think I'll get a few actually, Aisha might want one and if she doesn't, I'm sure someone else will.

Thursday - Fasting today was much better. At least I wasn't totally zoned out like last time! I broke my fast on some dates followed closely by a chocolate bar and coffee at work and had iftar properly at home. Irfan and Ali were fasting too - Irfan and his friends at the Islamic magazine he works for have decided to fast Mondays and Thursdays to get into Ramadan mode. Sometimes I really envy Irfan. It must be so amazing to work in an Islamic environment and have everyone encourage you! Oh well, I'll console myself with the fact that I must be getting more *thawab* fasting whilst having to watch Louise stuff her face at work.

Thawab: Reward

 Ayat and Ahadith

A'isha ⁕ reported that: "Whenever we were in menstruation period during the lifetime of the Prophet ⁕, he used to order us to make up for the days of fasting that we missed but he'd not order us to make up for the prayers we missed." (Bukhari and Muslim)

Sahl reported that the Prophet ⁕ said, "There is a gate in Paradise called Ar-Raiyan, and those who observe fasts will enter through it on the Day of Resurrection and none except them will enter through it. It will be said, 'Where are those who used to observe fasts?' They will get up, and none except them will enter through it. After their entry the gate will be closed and nobody will enter through it." (Bukhari)

6th Sha'ban - 3 weeks before the start of Ramadan

Saturday – 'Night Prayer' Week - Alhamdulillah, I managed to get everything I needed from the bookstore in the mosque. They've got such a large collection of books and I really need to read a lot more, but I just don't seem to have time to browse through them, especially if I go shopping with Fatima. I always promise myself never to go shopping with her again, but somehow I forget. She managed to drag me into 20 different shops as we looked for scarves for her friend who'd just started to cover her hair; at least it's for a good cause…

Wednesday - It's amazing how much you can learn from your younger siblings - apart from reading comic books, that is! Yesterday Ali and his friends stayed up all night organising a football tournament to raise money for charity. I walked in to find our living room wall blue-tacked with sheets of paper. Each sheet, and there were many, had lists of teams, game times, refs and groups. They'd even decided on the kit colours and knew exactly who was doing what…I feel quite ashamed that I haven't thought of something to generate charity myself yet – I'll have to put it down on my priority list of things to do. Talking of things to do, insha'Allah I'm going to start night prayers tonight. I really hope I manage to get up for *Tahajjud*. I should do, I'll only be waking up half an hour before I usually wake up for Fajr.

> **Tahajjud:** Nafl (voluntary) night time prayer

Thursday - I had 'one of those days' today! I had a number of things on at work and never really seemed to get it all out of the way – I hate having to wait on others to get things done. Oh, and Tahajjud, it's not as easy as it sounds…I kept snoozing my alarm until 2 minutes before Fajr which left me no time whatsoever. Well, no one said it was going to be easy, but then again maybe if I'd slept before 1am I would've had a better chance! I feel really bad about not getting up, but I managed to find this really cool article with all kinds of tips for performing night prayers - and yes, sleeping early was included there as well as saying *adhkar* before sleeping. I'll make sure

8

I get some form of *qiyam* done tonight by praying two rak'at after Isha, and still try to get up before Fajr. Insha'Allah tomorrow will be a better day.

P.S. Alhamdulillah fasting is going well. Only 1 more day and I'll have finished all my days from last year! I'm going to continue fasting Mondays and Thursdays though as Aisha told me today that the Prophet ﷺ used to fast a lot in Sha'ban as it is the month in which our deeds are presented to Allah.

> **Adhkar:** Specific du'a to be said in different situations
> **Qiyam:** Nafl (voluntary) night time prayer

> **Turn to:**
> • **Page 64** for more information on Night Prayer

Friday Morning - Wow! It really is a great feeling to have woken up at night. Surely all thanks is to Allah and then to Aisha! She promised yesterday that she would miss-call me to help me get up. Well she stuck to her word - she not only missed-called me, she practically woke up the whole house calling me on my mobile about five times. I'm really glad I got up though. Every time I read about the massive benefits of night prayer I feel bad that I haven't been doing it more frequently. I'm so in need of getting closer to Allah so, insha'Allah this will help.

> ❝ **Ayat and Ahadith**
>
> Usamah ibn Zayd ؓ was reported to have said that he asked the Prophet ﷺ, "I have not seen you observe additional fast during any month [other than Ramadan] as you do in Sha'ban?" He ﷺ replied, "This is a month that people usually forget about between Rajab and Ramadan, and it is a month in which people's deeds are presented to Allah, so I like that my deeds are presented while I am fasting." (An-Nasa'i)
>
> Salman al-Farsi ؓ quoted the Prophet ﷺ as saying: "Observe the Night Prayer; it was the practice of the righteous before you and it brings you closer to your Lord and it is penance for evil deeds and erases the sins and repels disease from the body." (At-Tabarani) ❞

13th Sha'ban - just over 2 weeks before the start of Ramadan

'Zakat and Sadaqah' Week

14th Sha'ban - I met up with a group of old friends from a Saturday school we used to attend, and we had a great meal at 'Mandarin House', this new Halal Chinese place that's opened up in town. It was good to see them all again as ever since we all started work it's been really difficult to get together. Trust us to get into heated discussions though…It all started with Hameeda saying that it was the night of the 15th of Sha'ban today and that we should be sure to pray at night and fast tomorrow. Then everyone started arguing about it not being totally right and that there are no authentic reports about fasting on that day. In the end we decided to ask a sheikh who said that there are many ahadith on the merit of the night and that there is no harm in increasing our worship and prayer on that night.

Monday - Alhamdulillah, my programme of night prayers is going well and I'm not at all tired at work. I've kind of got myself into a routine now. I get up about 40 minutes before Fajr, do 2 rak'at of Tahajjud and do istighfars till Fajr time. I then pray and get about an hour's sleep before I get up again. We've got this really huge brand presentation to the sales team on Friday, and the boss, Michael, is making us work our heads off! I just hope I can get through this manic week! I'm treating myself to a spa experience this weekend with Sabeena, I think it's brilliant that they have a ladies only day! At least the thought of that will get me through the week.

Wednesday - Ahh Wednesday – sometimes my favourite day of the week. In a weird way, I know that when I go to sleep, I'll wake up and it will be Thursday, which draws me all that closer to FRIDAY! That's a bit sad when I come to think about it, but I would give anything to get this presentation over and done with. I found some time to log into my bank account though and I've just realised that I'm due to pay *zakat* on the amount I've saved from last year - not that it's a fortune or anything but I've done the calculation and there is some money that I need to pay out. I wonder how I should spend it…I'll talk to Aisha about it.

> **Zakat:** The third pillar of Islam, this is the spending of a fixed portion of one's wealth for the poor or less fortunate

Thursday - I had to control myself and not completely lose it with Fatima today. I got back from work and decided to get my outfit ready for the presentation tomorrow so I wouldn't have to get up really early in the morning. I almost freaked out when I found out that she'd 'borrowed' the skirt I was going to wear and that she'd gone out with it for the evening! What did I do to deserve a 16-year-old sister who thinks my wardrobe is hers, is exactly my size and never asks! I tell you, it's a good thing the Islamic lecture I was listening to today mentioned charity in its various ways - and specifically lending your items. Speaking of charity, I must also make sure to set aside my *sadaqah* money for Ramadan…otherwise any extra money I have will probably end up with a similar fate as this weekend's spa trip…

P.S. Qur'an reading is going well, actually it's going ok, in fact it could be better. If it wasn't for my night prayers, I don't think I'd be getting anywhere near 3 pages. I'll make sure I sit and read at least 2 pages before I go to sleep.

> **Sadaqah:** Charity in its various forms

 Ayat and Ahadith

Alms are for the poor and the needy, and those employed to administer the (funds); for those whose hearts have been recently reconciled (to the Truth); for those in bondage and in debt; in the Cause of Allah; and for the wayfarer. Thus it is ordained by Allah, and Allah is full of knowledge and wisdom. (Surah At-Tawbah 9: 60)

Mu'adh ibn Jabal reported that the Prophet ﷺ said that, "Sadaqah extinguishes sin as water extinguishes fire." (At-Tirmidhi)

20th Sha'ban - 1 week before the start of Ramadan

Monday - 'Connecting with Family & Friends' week - Aaah, what a spa experience does to clear the mind…It also helps to have that brand presentation out of the way. At least now Michael won't drive me crazy with a million e-mails telling me this is the most important presentation of the year blah, blah, blah! Even Mum was getting worried about the time I'm spending at work, 'We never see you at home anymore'…Trust the preparation programme to make me feel even more guilty with it being 'Connecting with Family & Friends' week! Not to worry though, I'm thinking of arranging a huge family dinner and having Uncle Hussein give a talk about Ramadan afterwards. I'm sure I can convince everyone to come with my specialty brownies, and Mum loves bringing the family together. If only I could convince Fatima to do the cleaning - well she owes me one after last week's skirt abduction…

Tuesday - After consulting with Dad and most of my aunties and uncles, I've decided to have the dinner on Saturday. I read a nice piece in Irfan's magazine on how to make Ramadan an exciting time for the children by having lovely decorations and making small packages of simple Ramadan gifts. I couldn't believe it when I found a massive Ramadan corner at the supermarket the other day, with some beautifully packaged dates. I decided to put them in the Ramadan packages together with a Qur'an CD, some 'I love ALLAH' stickers and a 'Stories of the Prophets for Children' book, all from the Islamic bookstore.

Thursday - I love planning a big party…Ramadan dinner…I mean! It's such a shame that we all don't see each other all the time, but with everyone so busy, it really is impossible. Everything is under control for the dinner, everyone is coming, the Ramadan bags are all finished, I've decided on the menu and unbelievably Fatima will be helping out with the cleaning. There's nothing that girl won't do for chocolate! I mustn't forget to call and e-mail those members of the family that live abroad. It's always harder to stay in touch with those far away, but it's all worth it. I'm so happy I'm getting into *silat ar-rahm* before Ramadan as I know it really helps multiply your thawab! Well, it's getting my full attention this week!

> **Silat ar-Rahm:** Maintaining the ties of the womb (relations), visiting family and keeping in touch with them

Saturday - It has been such a good day. I can't stop smiling. Not because I managed to get the whole family together, but to see everyone laughing together and all the children having fun was just priceless (although I did come close to losing it with Abdurrahman, Uncle Hussein's son) – definitely a feel-good factor 10! We really should do it more often and Uncle Hussein's talk about Ramadan was really good too. Can't believe there are just 3 days left until Ramadan! It all comes at a price though – I'm soooo tired! Even though it's Sunday tomorrow and I have nothing on, I'm going to bed!

I've stopped my fasting as Ramadan is in just a couple of days and we shouldn't be fasting just before it.

 Do not fast the day before the announcement of Ramadan. Call and e-mail all your relatives to say Ramadan Mubarak.

❝ ❝ Ayat and Ahadith

Abu Huraira ﷺ reported that the Prophet ﷺ said, "None of you should fast a day or two before the month of Ramadan unless he has the habit of fasting (nawafil) (and if his fasting coincides with that day) then he can fast that day." (Bukhari)

Abu Huraira ﷺ reported that the Prophet ﷺ said, "Allah created the creations, and when He finished from His creations, Ar-Rahm i.e. womb, said, '(O Allah) at this place I seek refuge with You from all those who sever me (i.e. sever the ties of kith and kin)'. Allah said, 'Yes, won't you be pleased that I will keep good relations with the one who will keep good relations with you, and I will sever the relation with the one who will sever the relations with you?' It said, 'Yes, O my Lord.' Allah said, 'Then that is for you.'" Allah's Apostle ﷺ added, "Read (in the Qur'an) if you wish, the Statement of Allah: 'Would you then, if you were given the authority, do mischief in the land and sever your ties of kinship?' (47:22)"." (Bukhari)

❞ ❞

30th Sha'ban - The night before Ramadan

I had to squeeze this one in – it's official, Ramadan starts tomorrow! Subhanallah, the *shayateen* are actually chained now and the doors of Heaven are open and the doors of Hell are closed. Thinking about it like that really brings it to life! Must get ready as we're all going to the mosque for *Taraweeh* right away. Have to go, Dad's getting impatient, but I'll be back after Taraweeh.

> **Shayateen (plural of Shaytan):** Devils
> **Taraweeh:** Night prayers during Ramadan

After Taraweeh:

That was amazing. It really was. I think it's a lot different from last year as I'm switched on to the fact that it's Ramadan and have been working towards it for a few weeks now. It's also a little different this year because the imam that always prays with us has introduced something new; after the first 4 rak'at, he does a 'tip of the day' kind of thing. Tonight, he spoke about the Holy Qur'an and he mentioned the verse about how this is the month that the Qur'an was revealed in, Surah al-Baqarah I think it was. He stressed how we must have a special relationship with the Qur'an during this month. He's so right. If not this month, then when? I feel really guilty about ignoring the Qur'an these past few months. I haven't exactly been ignoring it, but just not giving it the attention it deserves. Oh Allah, please forgive me. I'm really going to try hard this month to get closer to You through the Qur'an, but I need Your help. Please help me to get closer to the Qur'an and to You this year.

The imam said that he knew it was difficult for most, but we should try and read one juz a day during Ramadan. Makes sense really – 30 days, 30 juz, even Fatima doesn't need a calculator for that! He said that some people read 2 juz a day and some of the *Sahabah* used to read 10 juz a night. I think I'll stick to reading one a day, or at least try, insha'Allah. Well I'm half way there already tonight. I'll read another quarter of a juz before I sleep and save the rest for Tahajjud! Sounds like a plan to me. Bedtime now – must wake up for Tahajjud and *suhoor* of course.

Sahabah: Companions of the Prophet Muhammad ﷺ

Suhoor: The meal consumed early in the morning before Fajr

 Ayat and Ahadith

Abu Huraira ؓ reported that Allah's Apostle ﷺ said, "When the month of Ramadan starts, the gates of the heaven are opened and the gates of Hell are closed and the devils are chained." (Bukhari)

O ye who believe, fasting is prescribed to you as it was prescribed to those before you, that ye may learn self-restraint. (Surah al-Baqarah 2:183)

Ramadan is the (month) in which was sent down the Qur'an, as a guide to mankind, and clear (Signs) for guidance and judgement (between right and wrong). So every one of you who is present (at his home) during that month should spend it in fasting. But if anyone is ill or on a journey, the prescribed period (should be made up) by days later. Allah intends every facility for you; He does not want to put you to difficulties. (He wants you) to complete the prescribed period, and to glorify Him! In that He has guided you; and perchance ye shall be grateful. (Surah al-Baqarah 2:185)

Ibn Umar narrated: I heard Allah's Apostle ﷺ saying, "When you see the crescent (of the month of Ramadan), start fasting, and when you see the crescent (of the month of Shawwal), stop fasting; and if the sky is overcast (and you can't see it) then regard the crescent (month) of Ramadan (as of 30 days)". (Bukhari)

And Ramadan Begins...

Day 1:

It really feels like it's Ramadan now. The check list and preparation did help, but actually having iftar together and going to Taraweeh afterwards has really made it come to life. My routine seems to be working too. I got up before Fajr for Tahajjud and had suhoor afterwards. I'd never really had a proper suhoor before; I used to always have water and sometimes coffee followed by a chocolate or something sad like that, but the sheikh mentioned that there is a blessing in taking a meal at that time - a little before dawn. I mustn't forget to make my *niyyah* for the fast otherwise it won't be valid!! He also mentioned that it was best to hasten the breaking of the fast (at least I've been doing something right all these years!). As soon as the clock turned 5:40, I kind of waited a minute, it was more like 10 seconds, just to be sure and then broke my fast with some dates according to the *sunnah* of the Prophet Muhammad ﷺ. I had some left over in my drawer at work from when I had started my fasting on Mondays and Thursdays in Sha'ban. I tried to get through a lot of du'as as I broke my fast since one of the times that du'a is accepted is at the time of breaking fast. It is also accepted throughout the day as one is fasting! Oh Allah, please accept my first day of fasting and all my days in Ramadan!

Last year, I put together an e-mail explaining a bit about Ramadan and its significance, and sent it out to everyone at work. Today, I dug it out of my sent messages folder and mailed it to the two new people at work who weren't here last year. It got people asking me questions about Ramadan which gave me a chance to explain a little. Russell, the new boy, was so surprised, 'You can't even drink water?' I get that question every year. I explained to him that during the fast time from Fajr to Maghrib we don't eat or drink anything, but that there were also spiritual dimensions to the fast. I specifically asked Michael to try not to schedule meetings at 5:30, as with his minimum 2 hour meetings there was no way I'd make it even to Taraweeh. Everyone was cool about it and as with every year, they asked a lot of questions about what happens and why we fast. This year I made sure that I read up on the basic fasting facts and so luckily I knew how to answer all their questions!

I love our first iftar together as a family. Dad always says, 'The first day is over and before we know it the whole month will be too, so make sure you use it properly.' It's a bit depressing to think of the end when it's just started, but at least it makes us appreciate the moment. Dad reminded everyone to say the du'a for breaking the fast and we had Mum's specialty tomato soup – extra spice. We don't usually have soup at dinner, but it's our Ramadan family tradition and I love it!

And Taraweeh – Taraweeh is just the best. The imam's voice is so good; it gets me right into the spirit of Ramadan. He really brings the surah to life masha'Allah and definitely helps me to focus more. I might be wrong, but the number of people that attend seems to increase every year. It's great to see so many Muslims in one place and people offering water to those praying during the break is always amazing. The imam spoke about the excellence of fasting today and told us that the reward for fasting is given by Allah as we leave eating, drinking and wrongdoing for His sake. It really is a great thawab, subhanallah. He also spoke about the importance of du'a, and how we should make the most of it. I really have tons of things that I need to pray for this year…

I must remember to tick off today's daily checklist, although I already know that I won't be getting any ticks for *da'wah* as I didn't get a chance to do that today. Hold on! Maybe my e-mail to people at work can be considered as da'wah.

Niyyah: Intention

Sunnah: The way of the Prophet ﷺ. They are the physical actions and sayings that were instituted by Prophet Muhammad ﷺ that we should follow in our daily lives

Da'wah: Calling to or inviting others to Islam or acts of worship or general good

Turn to:
- **Page 68** for draft e-mail that can be sent out to non-muslims

An example of an intention to fast (can be said at any time from sunset until just before dawn for the following day's fast):

وبصوم غد نويت من شهر رمضان

Wa bis sawmi ghadin nawaytu min shahri Ramadan

I intend to fast tomorrow in the month of Ramadan

Du'a when Breaking Fast

اللهم انى لك صمت وبك امنت وعلى رزقك أفطرت

Allahumma inni laka sumtu wa bika amantu wa 'ala rizqika aftartu

O Allah, I fasted for You and I believe in You and I break
my fast with Your sustenance (Abu Dawud)

ذهب الظمأ وابتلت العروق وثبت الأجر ان شاء الله

Dhahabadh-dhama'u wab-tallatil 'uruqi, wa thabatal ajru insha' Allah

Thirst has vanished, veins have moistened and Allah willing,
reward (for the fast) is certainly fixed (Abu Dawud)

> ❝❝ **Ayat and Ahadith**
>
> Allah's Apostle ﷺ said, "Three prayers are not rejected: the prayer of a father, the prayer of a fasting person, and the prayer of a traveller." (Al-Bayhaqi)
>
> Allah's Apostle ﷺ said, "The fasting person has at the time of breaking his fast a du'a that is not rejected." (Ibn Majah and Al-Hakim)
>
> Abu Huraira ؓ narrated that: Allah's Apostle ﷺ said, "Fasting is a shield (or a screen or a shelter). So, the person observing fasting should avoid sexual relations with his wife and should not behave foolishly and impudently, and if somebody fights with him or abuses him, he should tell him twice, 'I am fasting.'" The Prophet added, "By Him in Whose Hands my soul is, the smell coming out from the mouth of a fasting person is better in the sight of Allah than the smell of musk. (Allah says about the fasting person), 'He has left his food, drink and desires for My sake. The fast is for Me. So I will reward (the fasting person) for it and the reward of good deeds is multiplied ten times.'" (Bukhari)

Sahl bin Sad narrated that: Allah's Apostle ﷺ said, "The people will remain on the right path as long as they hasten the breaking of the fast." (Bukhari)

Anas ؓ reported Allah's Messenger ﷺ as saying: "Take meal a little before dawn, for there is a blessing in taking meal at that time." (Bukhari)

Salman ibn Amir Dhabi related that the Prophet ﷺ said: "Break your fast with dates, or else with water, for it is pure." (Abu Dawud and At-Tirmidhi)

Day 2:

I got this e-mail at work today from Sabeena to a YouTube link and I did the ultimate no-no and clicked it with my volume on full! What a way to attract attention. It made me feel bad as it gives the impression that you're not doing any work. I just seem to be so conscious about Michael thinking that I'm taking it easy because it's Ramadan – I hate giving a bad impression about Islam. I do put in a lot of effort at work and I'm glad to say that I'm not really one of those people that will spend about an hour checking my mail and then calling my mates, followed by a one hour lunch then an office gossiping session – alhamdulillah for that. I remember reading how that was so *haram* and it meant that you were doing two things: 1) cheating your employers and 2) gaining haram money! I most definitely don't want to be included in that band. May Allah make all our *rizq halal*, insha'Allah – a very important du'a.

Talking about du'a, I tried to focus on it today like the imam said yesterday but I realised that I had to put together a du'a plan because I wasn't really concentrating fully when I came to make du'a - not that I wasn't saying it, I was, but it just seemed to come out very randomly. I was trying to squeeze in du'as for myself, family and friends - even du'as for Sabeena to find a great husband and Aunty Zainab to be blessed with a child - in every *sajdah!* Obviously it wasn't working because either I spent ten minutes in my sajdah and by the time I got up I couldn't remember whether I was in my first or second sajdah, or I cut it short and didn't get all my du'as done. It was such a help when Sarah, from the Islamic Children in Need charity I'd recently started volunteering at, shared her du'a plan with me and it's such a cool idea. To begin with I wrote down all the du'as that I wanted to make and then put them into categories, so things like Jannah, Work, Family, Friends and the Ummah etc. I then chose a category to focus on in every rak'ah or after every salah. I'll follow this plan tomorrow, insha'Allah.

Subhanallah, the imam said that du'a is in fact worship and that's because by asking Allah for all the things you want you are acknowledging the Almighty's existence.

Fatima came home from school today looking awful. She had a really bad headache and looked very faint. It turns out that she'd taken part in a 500 metre race in PE and was obviously exhausted. Mum told her that she shouldn't take part in heavy running while she's fasting so she doesn't get so tired. She's going to school with her to speak to her teacher. Come to think of it, I remember Aisha mentioning that her brother's school had received some kind of guidelines on Ramadan from the Muslim Council to help make the teachers more aware of Ramadan. I'll ask Aisha to get me a copy of the guidelines and maybe Mum can take it to Fatima's teachers.

When I got home I managed to send a couple of e-mails to everyone in my address book with the checklist and some tips for actions in Ramadan. It's an easy form of da'wah but very effective. I'm sure they'll find it useful to follow.

Haram: Forbidden in Islam
Rizq: Sustenance, provision
Halal: Allowed/permissible in Islam
Sajdah: The act of prostration

Turn to:
- **Pages 70-72** for etiquette for making du'a and sample du'a plan
- **Page 74** for Guidelines for schools on Ramadan

 Ayat and Ahadith

The Prophet Muhammad ﷺ said, "Dua is the very essence of worship." (Nawawi, Abu Zakariyya Yahiya Ibn Sharaf Kitab al-Adhkar)

And your Lord says: "Call on Me; I will answer your (prayer). But those who are too arrogant to serve Me will surely find themselves in Hell - in humiliation." (Surah Mu'min 40: 60)

Day 3:

Alhamdulillah the du'a strategy is really working! I found myself having more time to say the du'a and I got through my entire list by the end of the day! It's really helped me focus on what I want to make du'a about. Well seeing that making a plan for du'a was so effective, I decided to apply the same strategy and make a sadaqah plan! I think I'm turning into a planning freak! There's an internal position going at work in the project management department – I might just have to consider it if this Ramadan is a success. Anyway, back to the sadaqah plan, it's all really simple actually. I just have to make sure I try and do something every day and tick off my checklist when I have. I went to the pound shop and picked up a massive piggy bank - *astaghfirullah* – it wasn't really a piggy, piggy bank if you know what I mean. More like a box with a big slot in it. I also bought a pack of sticky labels, and labelled one 'Daily Sadaqah' and stuck it on the boxy-bank. I put it in the living room and got Mum, Dad, Irfan, Fatima and Ali to buy into the idea. Basically, when we wake up in the morning we put in whatever we want to give away to charity that day - nothing is too small or too big. Then on Friday we take the money and put it in the charity box in the mosque or give it away to a good cause. It didn't take too much convincing to get everyone on board, especially when I emphasised nothing is too small and that the Prophet 鷺 was the most generous of people, and he used to become even more generous in Ramadan! I'm also going to make sure I include all kinds of sadaqah in the plan, not just the financial type and that means anything from smiling at people, speaking good words, helping people carry their shopping. Anything that means I am helping others really. The Prophet 鷺 even said that removing something 'harmful from the way' is considered a sadaqah – I wonder if removing Irfan's smelly trainers from the hallway would fit in to that category?

P.S. I also got a call from Souad, the chairman of the Islamic Children in Need charity and they want to arrange an iftar for the whole group this weekend. It's to be a one-dish party kind of iftar - I'd better start thinking of what I want to make! I have brownies on my mind - I always have brownies on my mind. Maybe I'll make a dessert and a main dish too! It's a bit sad, but I take it as one of my blessings that I'm really good in the kitchen.

Ayat and Ahadith

Ibn 'Abbas narrated that: The Prophet 🕊 was the most generous amongst the people, and he used to be more so in the month of Ramadan when Jibril visited him, and Jibril used to meet him on every night of Ramadan till the end of the month. The Prophet 🕊 used to recite the Holy Qur'an to Jibril, and when Jibril met him, he used to be more generous than a fast wind (which causes rain and welfare). (Bukhari)

So he who gives (in charity) and fears (Allah), and (in all sincerity) testifies to the Best, We will indeed make smooth for him the path to Bliss. But he who is a greedy miser and thinks himself self-sufficient, and gives the lie to the Best, We will indeed make smooth for him the path to Misery. (Surah al-Layl 92:5-10)

It is related that Abu Huraira 🕊 said that the Prophet 🕊 said, "There is no day which dawns on the slaves of Allah without two angels descending and one of them saying, 'O Allah, refund those who give money' and the other saying, 'O Allah, ruin those who withhold it.'" (Bukhari)

"There is a (compulsory) sadaqah (charity) to be given for every joint of the human body (as a sign of gratitude to Allah) everyday the sun rises. To judge justly between two persons is regarded as sadaqah; and to help a man concerning his riding animal, by helping him to mount it or by lifting his luggage on to it, is also regarded as sadaqah; and (saying) a good word is also sadaqah; and every step taken on one's way to offer the compulsory prayer (in the mosque) is also sadaqah; and to remove a harmful thing from the way is also sadaqah." (Bukhari and Muslim)

Day 4:

I picked up the charity box this morning before I went to work and it was really heavy. I had no idea who had put what in it, but I did a bit of investigating when I got home and found out, through Mum, that Fatima had been putting aside £1 a week for the last few weeks as she wanted to buy an iPod and decided instead that she would give her money to charity during this Ramadan. Masha'Allah, I'm so proud of her. I decided with Mum that we'll both chip in and get her one for Eid. Just goes to show that you can't judge people, even if you know them (or think you know them) very well.

It's a good thing I started getting used to fasting a couple of weeks before Ramadan! Some people I know are still struggling and others are just starting to get the hang of it. I also owe a lot to an article I read in Irfan's magazine. I had a complete change of strategy for suhoor and wow, it really worked! The article was all about healthy eating when fasting and there were some really cool tips. It advised against over-eating at suhoor, but I don't have to worry about that, it was probably targeted at the likes of Irfan! It did say though that we should try to eat slow digesting foods that contain grains and seeds, and that bananas are excellent too, so I got two family size packs of muesli to last me for the next few days and had a large bowl with milk and some dates. It filled me up for the whole day – well almost! The article also warned about over-eating at iftar – I guess everyone has done that before. It ruins the rest of the day when that happens and you definitely can't concentrate in Taraweeh.

Taraweeh was amazing as usual. The imam talked about da'wah and really encouraging friends to take part in activities and worship with you. I have to admit I'm really bad with that one so I need to work on it. I mean Safa and Huma, two of my friends that I used to go to school with, are always complaining about how they find it difficult to go to the mosque for Taraweeh and that they don't always pray it at home. I guess I could have an iftar at my place and take them to Taraweeh with me. I'll call them tomorrow and see when they can come.

Turn to:
- **Page 75** for Health guidelines on eating in Ramadan

66 **Ayat and Ahadith**

Ibn Umar reported Allah's Messenger 🕌 as saying: "A believer eats in one intestine (i.e. he is satisfied with a little food), whereas a non-believer eats in seven intestines (eats much)."(Muslim)

…eat and drink but waste not by excess, for Allah loveth not the wasters. (Surah Al-Araf 7: 31)

Invite friends around that don't go to Taraweeh but you feel might if you encourage them and take them along with you. Be tactful!

Day 5:

There I go again, thinking I know it all and finding out that I actually have no idea! I found out today that there are actually three levels of fasting: 'ordinary', 'special' and 'extra-special'. I'm having to struggle with my ego on this one, but it turns out that I'm kind of fitting into the 'special' fasting this year, alhamdulillah. I'm not going to get too excited though as I think I only fit into it sometimes rather than all the time. I think my total TV ban and my Qur'an only iPod has been a positive step towards the special section. I would've loved to be in the 'extra-special' level but you have to rid yourself of all unworthy concerns to be right up there, so I guess I still have quite a bit to do in that department.

For a while now, I've wanted to do some kind of community work and I spent all morning racking my brain to find something that I could possibly get involved in. I was starting to get depressed when out of the blue, Aisha called and told me about the children's hospital! Aisha's little cousin was sick last year and had to spend two weeks there and Aisha's been volunteering there ever since. We ended up taking 'My Little Pony' toys for the girls and 'Power Ranger' figures for the boys and spent some quality time with the children. I took loads of prawn cocktail crisps and M&Ms but the nurse at the door confiscated them - not the best of ideas I have to admit. I'm so glad that Allah gave me the opportunity to go though, it's a real eye-opener to see what other people have to go through; makes you say alhamdulillah several times. And to be able to do this in Ramadan is a complete bonus! Just goes to show that with Allah you just need to take a step and He'll help you with the rest, subhanallah.

Alhamdulillah I called Safa and Huma today and they can both make next Tuesday. Just have to tell Mum to make iftar for two more people, I'm sure it'll be no problem as she always over-cooks anyway. Talking about cooking, I think I've decided to go for chicken biryani for the charity dinner, I think

I'll skip the brownies and save them for another time. Must remember to either pick the chicken up from the butchers or send Fatima to go and get some for me, I know which one I'd rather.

Turn to:
• **Page 76** for the three levels of fasting

> 66 **Ayat and Ahadith**
>
> "Look at those who are less fortunate than you, and don't look at those who are more fortunate than you. This would be more appropriate, that you don't disregard Allah's *ni'mah* (blessings) upon you." (Muslim) 99

Day 6:

I always thought Fridays were special, but I have to admit it was more because it was the start of the weekend, and not because I knew that we should consider it a day of Eid! The imam mentioned though that we should follow the Islamic etiquette of Friday by doing certain activities on that day. There's a great section of some things we should do in Imam Ghazali's book, *Ihya Ulum ad-Din*, 'Revival of the Religious Sciences'. I think the imam kind of felt that it would be a bit difficult for everyone to go and read the book so he decided to give us a head start and highlight what we should do! I made sure I did *ghusl* when I woke up and listened to Surah al-Kahf on my way into work. I also tried to get in as many *salat alar-Rasool* during the day. I'd never known before that that was the day when the Prophet ﷺ looks at how many times we've prayed upon him! Now that I'm not going out for lunch break, I've decided to spend about ten minutes before 'Asr in the first aid room where I pray at work and get in some du'as before salah. Some scholars say that it might be the hour of acceptance. I also remembered to take our family boxy-bank to Taraweeh today and put the contents in the sadaqah box at the mosque! I was really quite impressed by how much there was - I never thought it would add up like that, alhamdulillah!

I was on the verge of starvation today - ok that's an exaggeration but honestly my stomach was rumbling so loudly I thought everyone at the office could hear it. And just to add to that, Claire walked in in the morning with half a dozen doughnuts and started offering them around. It really does get you thinking though of what it would be like if you actually had to go without proper food for days - not just doughnuts. It gave me the motivation to log on to an Islamic charity website and make an online donation to their food programmes in other countries. May Allah accept our deeds.

> **Ghusl:** Full ablution (ritual washing)
> **Salat alar-Rasool:** Praying upon the Prophet ﷺ

Turn to:
- **Page 77** for Etiquette of Friday and actions to be undertaken on that day

  Ayat and Ahadith

On one Friday, Rasulullah ﷺ said: "O Muslims! Allah Ta'ala has made this day a day of Eid. So have a bath on this day, whoever has perfume should apply it, and use the miswaak." (Ibn Majah)

Day 7: Weekend, Yes!!

Charity Dinner! I spent the morning making three pans of chicken biryani - enough to feed 20 people. The state of the kitchen left much to be desired, but Mum was feeling charitable and said she'd take over the cleaning! I managed to call Shaima, my neighbour, and get her to come along with me - I'm always trying to get her involved in these events and she was very excited about it. Masha'Allah it was such an eventful day and Souad had really gone out of her way by putting everything together. She had organised the iftar at the Community Centre and had invited a sheikh to give a lecture about Ramadan. He reminded us that we were in the first ten days of *rahmah* and that we should really work to attain Allah's mercy. This would help us in the following ten days of forgiveness and the last ten days which are freedom from Hellfire - I really want to focus on that du'a: May Allah liberate us from Hellfire! The food was amazing and everyone had really gone out of their way to make the best food they could - it was the nicest feeling of togetherness I've felt in ages! I also managed to bring three big packs of dates from the local store - a cunning idea of mine to make sure that everyone breaks their fast first on what I brought to get thawab of feeding a fasting person! Seeing all the happy faces of my sisters in Islam, Sabeena, Aisha, Souad and all the rest was amazing. It's always great to be around this good group of friends. We all prayed Taraweeh together at the mosque in the centre. We're also planning a bazaar to raise money for those less fortunate than us. Another great opportunity to get thawab in Ramadan - can't wait!

> **Rahmah:** Mercy

> **❝ Ayat and Ahadith**
>
> Salman al-Farsi reported that the Prophet Muhammad ﷺ said: "If anyone provides a fasting person with an iftar meal, Allah will forgive his sins, and save him from Hell-fire (in the Hereafter), and he will have a reward equal to the fasting person without reducing the reward deserved for him." Some Companions said: "Not all of us can afford to give an iftar to a fasting person." The Prophet then remarked: "Indeed, Allah gives such great reward to any one who provides iftar to a fasting person even if it is a date, a sip of water, or a jar of milk…" (Ibn Khuzaymah from the Prophet's sermon on Ramadan) **❞**

Day 8:

After my success with the biryani yesterday, I volunteered to cook iftar at home today. Obviously I wanted the thawab of feeding fasting people but I also wanted to give Mum a day off – it was the least I could do after all the hard work she put in cleaning the kitchen yesterday! I made some delicious tomato soup (Mum's recipe of course), vegetable lasagna and sweet and sour lamb chops - even Ali was all compliments. I think I'm fast becoming the Muslim Delia Smith. I didn't make dessert, not because I couldn't be bothered or anything but I wanted everyone to eat light so that they weren't too full to pray Taraweeh! I also helped Dad with some filing for his papers that he'd been telling me about for a week now. I really should help out at home a lot more - and not only at the weekends. Well, today was a start!

I've been keen to get Fatima and Ali involved in all the Ramadan activities that have been going on for some time, so I took Fatima to the iftar with me yesterday, and I'm getting them both involved in the bazaar, but I want them to get into the Ramadan zone that I'm experiencing. I've decided to get them to fill their own trackers and to have a kind of update with each other every couple of days so that we're all getting most things done. Ali is so competitive and always wants to beat us in anything we do! If I tell him I've done 100 istighfars, he goes and does 200! It's an easy way of making sure he gets thawab.

I also got round to calling some relatives abroad to say Ramadan Mubarak - bit late I know but better late than never! I couldn't get through to everyone, so I sent some text messages too. Not everyone replied straight away. I'm sure they're all just busy with Ramadan things themselves. Will make sure I call them all on Eid, insha'Allah.

 Tip: Try to call as many members of the family as you can, especially ones that you don't get to speak to so often.

Day 9:

I almost had a heart attack when I was calculating the days I'm not going to fast on and thought it was going to be in the last ten days! Alhamdulillah I'll just have finished before the 20th of Ramadan…hopefully. I know that it's from Allah but I'd rather be at the mosque doing Taraweeh! I've decided to book a weeks holiday from work - 3 in the last ten days and 2 days for Eid. I sent Michael an e-mail with my holiday request and he wrote back straight away saying it was fine! Good, at least that's sorted.

Someone was giving out a little handbook at the mosque today which had all the adhkar that one should say in all the different situations. Subhanallah! Some people are always ready with things to do to get thawab! Why can't it be me? I flicked through it and there are adhkar to say when you're driving, when you get up in the morning, as you enter and leave the mosque and loads of other ones too. I'd better keep it with me all the time and try and remember to say them! Wow, to think that I could get thawab even as I'm going into the bathroom!!

Anyway, the imam's talk yesterday was about reflection and contemplation. To tell you the truth, I've never really understood what and how we should do that. The imam said that in the Qur'an we are always being asked to look at the heavens and the earth, and at ourselves and that will help us to increase our faith and our knowledge of Allah and His greatness. I would love to book myself a trip to New Zealand; the scenery, everyone tells me, is the most beautiful on earth! Given the time and my tight budget though, I thought of another, no doubt less glamorous way of doing this form of worship. I searched for some pictures on the internet of landscapes and wildlife, and honestly they were really breathtaking. I put them on slideshow and was staring at my screen saying subhanallah every 2 seconds. Fatima came into the room in the middle of all that and gave me her, 'What are you doing/eyebrows crossed' kind of look. I filled her in and then there were two chairs in front of the monitor saying "Subhanallah, subhanallah, subhanallah"!

Turn to:
• **Page 80-81** for Article on contemplation

 Ayat and Ahadith

In the creation of the heavens and the earth and the alternation of night and day, there are signs for people with intelligence: those who remember Allah, standing, sitting and lying on their sides, and reflect on the creation of the heavens and the earth: "Our Lord, You have not created this for nothing. Glory be to You! So safeguard us from the punishment of the Fire." (Surah Al 'Imran 3: 190-191)

 Get a book of Adhkar and keep it with you at all times.

Day 10:

There were plenty of cakes and snacks at the office today as it was one of our sales guys' last day. Everyone was being very apologetic about the food, but I told them not to worry - I'd stock up and have it later! I want to focus on my khushoo' again, as I still feel that my prayers are a bit rushed. I just think that I need to give myself a bit more time to complete them and try shutting everything else out of my mind.

I've been praying all my *sunnah prayers* though, which is great, alhamdulillah. The imam mentioned that there were 12 rak'at of sunnah *al-mu'akkadah* prayers with the five fard prayers that one should do. He also went on for ages about the *Doha prayer* and the benefits of doing it! I decided to pray it before I left for work in the morning and that was a great achievement given the daily rush I am always in to leave the house and get into the car.

I did a kind of self reflection and evaluation of myself today – I can't believe the first 10 days are already gone! I went through the daily checklist and looked at how many boxes I'd ticked off every day. Not too bad I'd say but there are still major areas that I need to focus on. I need to bring my Qur'an up to date as I'm falling a bit behind and I have to do a complete reading of the Qur'an this Ramadan insha'Allah as it's one of my goals. I also want to really reflect on what I'm reading. I think I'll start reading a bit of *tafsir* every day as well. Aisha told me that she keeps a notebook beside her every time she reads the Qur'an and writes down her reflections and questions that she'd like to ask and what she has learnt. I think I should do the same.

Tomorrow's the first day of the ten days of *maghfirah!* I am so in need of Allah's forgiveness! The Prophet Muhammad ﷺ used to do istighfars around 70 times a day and some reported 100 times a day! And there's me, queen Ameena, who probably does about 3 istighfars a week outside Ramadan. I'll make sure I do a lot over these next ten days.

There's a hadith about it being a tragedy for anyone to make it through Ramadan and not gain Allah's forgiveness. I hope I'm one of the ones that do, insha'Allah.

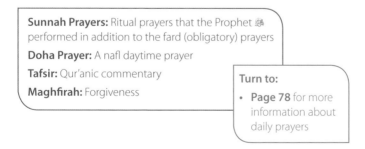

Sunnah Prayers: Ritual prayers that the Prophet ﷺ performed in addition to the fard (obligatory) prayers

Doha Prayer: A nafl daytime prayer

Tafsir: Qur'anic commentary

Maghfirah: Forgiveness

Turn to:
• **Page 78** for more information about daily prayers

> ❝ **Ayat and Ahadith**
>
> The Prophet ﷺ said: "He who assiduously performs twelve rak'at (prayer units), will have a house built for him in Paradise. They are: four rak'at before the afternoon prayer (Dhuhr) and two rak'at after it; two rak'at after the sunset prayer (Maghrib); two rak'at after evening prayer (Al-`Isha'); and two rak'at before the dawn prayer (Fajr)." (At-Tirmidhi)
>
> The Prophet ﷺ made it clear that, "If any Muslim comes out of Ramadan without gaining forgiveness and goodness, he/she is a real loser." (Ibn Hibban and At-Tabarani) ❞

Day 11:

I had a great idea today! I woke up and said, "I'm going to make this day 'Salat alar-Rasool day'". The idea, very simply put, was to send salutations upon the Prophet ﷺ every free moment of the day that I had. I must've said the Salat alar-Rasool about 500 times masha'Allah. As I went into work today, as I went down to pray, and as I did my filing at work I kept on saying it. Subhanallah it really helps you connect with the Prophet ﷺ and it also brings this calming feeling to the soul.

I've been trying to remind myself to follow in the footsteps of the Prophet ﷺ in most things I do. I remember to say the du'a before eating and to drink in the right way, but there are so many other things that I forget or didn't know that I should do. I'm going to try and start reading about the sunnan of the Prophet ﷺ and try and implement as many as I can.

Sabeena called to invite me for iftar with her family this Saturday. Her sister Sabah will be there and will bring little Khadeejah with her! She must've grown since the last time I saw her. Sabah is doing her Taraweeh at home this year because with Khadeejah's crying neither she nor anyone else will be able to concentrate in prayer. She's totally right though. We were going to complain at the mosque about the number of children running about. I'm not saying that they shouldn't come but there must be some way to get them to sit quietly while we pray. I'll try to think of something.

Tip: Start reading books about the sunnan of the Prophet and try to put these into practice in your daily life.

> > **Ayat and Ahadith**
>
> Allah Almighty says: "Lo! Allah and His angels shower blessings on the Prophet. O ye who believe! Ask blessings on him and salute him with a worthy salutation." (Surah Al-Ahzab 33:56)
> "

Day 12:

I hate it when that happens! You're sitting at your desk working happily away, minding your own business and the conversation suddenly drifts to the latest office gossip. Sarah from finance put a file on Louise's desk and said, "There you go, my dear". That triggered off a major mickey-taking session as soon as she turned away about the way she said that and it slowly drifted onto "Have you seen the way she eats her lunch?" thanks to Karen. I'm always the one to go, "Come on children, grow up – there's no need to be nasty now". After 5 minutes of trying to get them to change the topic and saying to myself, 'I am fasting', I decided to get up and go to the ladies. By the time I got back everyone had gone back to doing their work.

I felt really bad earlier for a bit about getting into a fight with Irfan, well not really a fight - more like a heated argument. He can really wind me up sometimes, that boy. All I did was ask him to Hoover in the hallway to help out and he said, "Do I look like a girl to you? Why don't you get Fatima to do it?" I felt like twisting his ear until he caved in and did what I said, but I didn't do that – instead I momentarily lost it on him, "IRFAN! Stop being lazy and do something for once in your life". I sort of noticed mid shouting that it's Ramadan and there's really no need to waste my fast on Irfan. Subhanallah that is why Allah said that Ramadan has been sent to us to help us exercise restraint! I made myself feel better by doing the vacuuming myself and making my intention for the sake of Allah and taking a load off Mum.

Anyway the imam mentioned today that if someone prays Fajr and then sits and does dhikr till sunrise, then prays two rak'at, they actually get thawab of an 'Umrah and Hajj! Wow, now that is simply amazing. I'm definitely planning to do that this weekend, insha'Allah.

> **'Umrah:** The 'lesser pilgrimage' that can be undertaken at any time of year
>
> **Hajj:** The fifth pillar of Islam, the major pilgrimage to Makkah

 Ayat and Ahadith

Abu Huraira ⚬ narrated that the Prophet ⚬ said: "Whoever does not give up forged speech and evil actions, Allah is not in need of his leaving his food and drink (i.e. Allah will not accept his fasting.)" (Bukhari)

Anas ⚬ narrated that the Prophet ⚬ said: "Whoever prays the Fajr prayer in congregation, then sits in dhikr (glorification of Allah) until the sun rises and then prays two rak'at, gets the reward of a Hajj and 'Umrah that are complete, complete, complete." (At-Tirmidhi)

Day 13:

I got into the office 15 minutes late today. Parking outside our house has become ridiculous. For some reason everyone just seems to come and dump their car outside our house and leave it there for days. Today, I found a car parked right outside our driveway blocking me in! I walked around frantically for 5 minutes until a guy in a suit who had been dropping his children off at the local school showed up. The fact that he was away for 5 minutes helped me to keep my cool and remind myself that I'm fasting.

Michael gave me the 'Why are you late look?' as I walked in and I explained the parking episode. I should've called to tell him I would be late, but I was trying to get out of traffic and thought I wouldn't be that late. I don't want him to think it's because of the fasting though. It's just a coincidence that it's happened twice this week - I'm never usually like that. Must make sure to get up really early tomorrow, just in case.

I met this really cool girl called Hannah at Taraweeh tonight. We were praying next to each other and then when the imam broke for the talk we had a quick chat. Turns out she works just down the road from me - what a small world! After prayers we got to talking about Ramadan and how it was going for her, and she said that the only thing that she really hates is the office! Of course I told her my whole episode with Louise and the girls, and she said it was always like that for her! Well it's good to know that I'm not alone in the struggle! Anyway, she's having an iftar at her house this Sunday for a group of her friends and has invited me to come along and get introduced to them all. I told her I'd check whether there were any family commitments or anything - you know how it is, Mum telling you on Sunday at 2pm that we're going to Aunty Zainab's or something - and I'd get back to her tomorrow. I don't know whether I should go or not…I don't really know anyone there and don't know what they're going to be like. I mean, I'm sure they're amazing people, but I don't want to be sitting alone at iftar looking like the girl they invited by mistake.

Day 14: Weekend, Yes, Yes!!

Masha'Allah, I managed to stay up till sunrise! Not as easy as it sounds though. I really had to stop myself drifting off to sleep in the last twenty minutes. I think you really need to do it with someone to get them to encourage you till the end. But it was worth it for the thawab – May Allah accept it, insha'Allah.

I've decided I will go to Hannah's iftar, after all. She seems like a great girl and I'm sure iftar at her place will be different from the usual. Must call or send her a text tomorrow morning to confirm.

I spent a good part of the morning in the loft bringing down our old books and toys – those that were in good condition of course - for the bazaar tomorrow. Everyone gave away something, Mum gave me a few of her amazing silk scarves, and even Irfan was kind enough to give away his Playstation 2. Must make sure I get to the mosque by 9am tomorrow to help set everything up. Waking Irfan up to help load everything into his car will be a nightmare. I know that boy well – waking him up early on a weekend is mission impossible.

Irfan got us all to sit together today and read Qur'an, each one reading from their own chapters and where they had last stopped. We did this from 'Asr to just before Maghrib. Dad then said the du'a and we all sat through it together. It was an amazing feeling to do *ibadah* all together! I'm so jealous of Irfan (in the good Islamic form of jealousy I mean!) because I've been trying to get us all to do something great as a family together. He's alright sometimes. Masha'Allah, I'm glad we managed to do something. We have to make sure we do it more often though.

Oh Allah, I HOPE I have attained your forgiveness. I keep reminding myself that we are in the days of maghfirah. There are actually three different ahadith telling us of three things to do in Ramadan to get our sins forgiven: fasting, doing qiyam, and doing qiyam on Laylat al-Qadr! I hope I can do all three!

I've thought of something to help with the children at the mosque during Taraweeh. I'm going to suggest that one of the classrooms they do weekend classes in be designated as the children's room and have one of the girls who is not praying look after them while their mothers pray. I'll speak to Hajar, the mosque co-ordinator, about it tomorrow.

> **Ibadah:** Worship

 Ayat and Ahadith

Abu Huraira ⁂ narrated that Allah's Apostle ⁂ said: "Whoever observes fasts during the month of Ramadan out of sincere faith, and hoping to attain Allah's rewards, then all his past sins will be forgiven." (Bukhari)

Abu Huraira ⁂ narrated that Allah's Apostle ⁂ said: "Whoever establishes the prayers on the night of Qadr out of sincere faith and hoping to attain Allah's rewards (not to show off) then all his past sins will be forgiven." (Bukhari)

Abu Huraira ⁂ narrated that Allah's Apostle ⁂ said: "Whoever fasted the month of Ramadan out of sincere faith (i.e. belief) and hoping for a reward from Allah, then all his past sins will be forgiven, and whoever stood for the prayers in the night of Qadr out of sincere faith and hoping for a reward from Allah, then all his previous sins will be forgiven." (Bukhari)

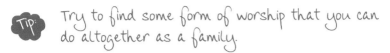

Tip: Try to find some form of worship that you can do altogether as a family.

Day 15:

Souad just called me and told me that the final count on the money raised was £5,204! Ramadan really does bring out the best in people – masha'Allah, I'm so pleased. I hope Allah accepts our deeds. We managed to sell almost everything and all of the stuff that came from our house was gone in the first hour. I really do hope it makes a difference to the lives of our less fortunate brothers and sisters both here and abroad.

Everyone's suddenly gone into iftar overdrive. I got 4 calls for iftar invites for the next 3 days and 2 calls for invites for next week. I think everyone's just realised that we're more than halfway through Ramadan now and they'd better get their day in. I don't mind these iftars, don't get me wrong, but they somehow transform into a party atmosphere with a lot of socialising, way too much food and getting to Taraweeh after the first two rak'at.

I'm really glad I went to Hannah's today though. It really was special. Now that's the kind of iftar you get from people you know from the mosque. Masha'Allah we all said du'a together, broke our fast on dates and then prayed Maghrib *jama'a*. We all sat together and had iftar in a circle so everyone could talk to each other. Her mum gave us a very short lecture and we all made our way to Taraweeh together. Hannah introduced me to her friends from a Monday tafsir circle that they have together. She's asked me to join them! That is so exciting! They've stopped for Ramadan though and will be picking it up after. I'll definitely start going when it's back on insha'Allah. I'm so happy I went.

I spoke to Hajar about the dealing-with-the-children idea and she loved it! She's been getting lots of complaints so at least that will partially solve it, insha'Allah. I'll go to the mosque early tomorrow to help her set up the space.

Jama'a: Congregation

37

Try and help out with keeping the children in place at your local mosque.

 If you get invited to an iftar then try to keep focused and in Ramadan mode. Make sure you leave early for Taraweeh.

Day 16:

I woke up feeling very sluggish today and kind of hungry even though I'd had a proper suhoor. It didn't really help that it was Monday morning. The feeling continued all day at work and I didn't manage to get out of it. I hate it when that happens. I knew it was bound to happen sometime as the imam had mentioned that no matter how excited and enthusiastic you are, you are bound to experience some kind of slowdown. That's why we always have to ask Allah for *thabat*. I dug out the du'a and said it a couple of times and tried to concentrate in prayer.

Work was slower than slow today which made it even worse. I must've looked at my watch about 100 times. Claire was away on a sales meeting and Louise had called in sick. It had that 'ghost town' feel to it which didn't help. I also hadn't heard anything from Aisha for the last couple of days, which was totally weird as we speak at least once a day, and she hadn't responded to my voicemail. I rang her up at home after iftar and her mum said that she was very sick with the flu. I hope she feels better soon. Will call her mum to ask if it's ok to drop by tomorrow to see how she is. There's great thawab for visiting a fellow Muslim who's sick, even greater during Ramadan.

I've never really appreciated food like I have today. OK, I was very hungry, more often than not, but sometimes in our lives certain things hit home. Today was my day for thanking Allah for blessing me and my family with food. Subhanallah, I think I'm beginning to understand the importance of fasting! It really is a great joy that you feel as you break your fast, being given the energy by Allah to complete the fast as the Prophet ﷺ said. I had to remind myself about not over-eating though. With the tiredness I'd been going through all day, I didn't want to take it with me to the mosque! Tarweeh's just too precious to waste on a bloated stomach.

Felt a bit better at the mosque and Hajar and I put together several partitions to make the room area. Hajar had printed all the labels 'Children's room', put up notices for mothers to make sure that their children sat in the room and spent the whole night guiding mothers with little ones to that area. Masha' Allah, Taraweeh was a lot better and it was much easier to concentrate.

Du'a for thabat

اللهم يا مقلب القلوب ثبت قلبى على دينك

Allahumma Ya Muqallib al-quloob, thabit qalbi ala deenik

O Controller of the hearts make my heart steadfast in Your religion

Thabat: Continuing on the straight path, steadfastness

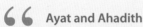 **Ayat and Ahadith**

Abu Huraira ◈ reported that Allah's Messenger ◈ said: "Every (good) deed of the son of Adam would be multiplied, a good deed receiving a tenfold to seven hundredfold reward, Allah, the Exalted and Majestic, has said, with the exception of fasting, for it is done for Me and I will give a reward for it, for one abandons his passion and food for My sake. There are two occasions of joy for one who fasts, joy when he breaks it, and joy when he meets his Lord, and the breath (of an observer of fast) is sweeter to Allah than the fragrance of musk." (Muslim)

Day 17:

My cramps started around midday today. It got really bad by the time I was leaving work, and by the time I got home I was knackered. No Taraweeh for the next few days. I'm really going to miss it! And the tip of the day! I'll get Fatima to fill me in on what's been said every night though. I think I'll call Sabeena too, she usually takes notes. I'd even seen some girls recording what the imam was saying on MP3 players - shame I don't know any of them personally.

I called Aisha's mum and she said that Aisha was feeling better and I can pass by her tomorrow. I'll get her some of her favourite chocolates on the way.

I thought I'd catch up on reading some tafsir as I had plenty of evening time with no Taraweeh to go to. I started reading tafsir of the 30th Juz and wow, I really did learn a lot. It makes a huge difference to understand the meaning of the surahs that you are reading in salah. It felt a bit lonely around the house with everyone at Taraweeh. Can't complain, it's from Allah that I'm off for the next couple of days. I remember last year I spent it all watching sitcoms on TV and feeling sorry for myself. What a waste of time that was!

But I need to think of some other things that I can do to maintain my Ramadan mode seeing that I'm neither fasting nor praying. If I had to be honest with myself, I'm a bit of TV addict, but I am determined not to watch TV during Ramadan. So I thought I'd read that book that I got from the Islamic bookstore but hadn't got round to reading yet. It's about the importance of purifying one's heart from diseases such as jealousy and arrogance. It mentioned that one way to help us to purify ourselves is to make a list of all we can remember from Allah's blessings upon us. Then make a list of all the sins we have committed. Comparing the two will help us feel Allah's blessings upon us and how undeserving and ungrateful we can be. Subhanallah, writing down all of Allah's blessings could take forever; even my attention to Ramadan and wanting to do something amazing in itself is a huge blessing!

 Tip: Make a list of Allah's blessings upon you and the sins you have committed.

Turn to:
• **Page 82** for What to do while you are menstruating

 Tip: Don't waste your non praying / fasting days on non Islamic matters. Instead do Tasbeehs remembering the blessings, do Istighfars remembering the sins.

Day 18:

Oh no, exactly what I was dreading. I have to go to this function for work tomorrow evening. I tried to get out of it but Michael insisted that I attend the presentation. I made it clear though that I wouldn't be staying for the after party. I spoke to Sarah today about how she managed to minimise interaction with the opposite sex at work. If anyone is able to give advice in that department it's her as she's an engineer and she's practically the only girl where she works. Anyway she told me that she tries her best to minimise 'work small talk' as she calls it. She basically doesn't get involved in meaningless chatter and tries not to talk about any topics not related to work. Not that she isolates herself; she is nice and friendly with everyone and gets involved in other conversations like what's happening in the news and stuff but as soon as it begins to drift into people she doesn't really get involved. Anyway, I'm going to try cutting out 'work small talk' for a while and see what happens. I told her that she is so lucky because guys don't gossip as much. She just gave me this look that said: they gossip like you wouldn't believe!

 Ayat and Ahadith

Part of someone's being a good Muslim is his leaving alone that which does not concern him. (At-Tirmidhi)

Day 19:

Alhamdulillah the function was OK. I managed to sit with Claire and Louise for the presentation and have some party snacks and then quickly disappeared. Good thing I wasn't praying as I would've been really upset if I had had to miss Taraweeh for something like that.

I made my way to Taraweeh as it was my turn to look after the children today. I was actually dreading it in the morning and had visions of 53 children all crying at the same time. Alhamdulillah it wasn't too bad, except for one little 6-year-old who didn't stop running from the moment he came in and decided that it would be fun to punch a few of the children and kick the rest. I managed to handle it though, the experience I've had with my two brothers was more than enough to help.

Can't believe that we're starting the last ten days tomorrow! Subhanallah and Laylat al-Qadr!

I know I told myself that I wouldn't be upset if I still couldn't fast and pray in the last ten days but I still wish I could've gone to Taraweeh today! I have to say alhamdulillah though I'll be finished tomorrow and so haven't missed that much - poor Sabeena, she's just started today! She was almost in tears wailing to me on the phone, 'I can't fast or pray, what am I supposed to do?' I tried to make her feel better (although I have to admit I felt so sorry for her) and told her that there were so many other things she could do like charity stuff, visiting family, listening to lectures, saying adhkar and du'a. I think she accepted the situation in the end though.

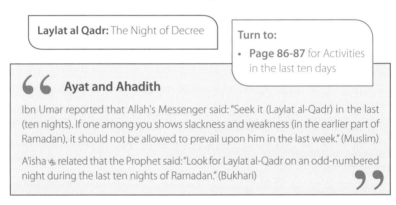

Laylat al Qadr: The Night of Decree

Turn to:
- **Page 86-87** for Activities in the last ten days

66 **Ayat and Ahadith**

Ibn Umar reported that Allah's Messenger said: "Seek it (Laylat al-Qadr) in the last (ten nights). If one among you shows slackness and weakness (in the earlier part of Ramadan), it should not be allowed to prevail upon him in the last week." (Muslim)

A'isha ◈ related that the Prophet said: "Look for Laylat al-Qadr on an odd-numbered night during the last ten nights of Ramadan." (Bukhari) **99**

Day 20:

Tonight is the night of the 21st. I can't believe that it could actually be Laylat al-Qadr as the Prophet ◈ told us to watch out for it specifically in the odd nights of the last ten days of Ramadan!

I was reading about Laylat al-Qadr today to get myself in the right frame of mind. I always knew that it was so important but today it really hit home. Oh Allah, please make me from the ones who witness the night! It is the night when the Qur'an was revealed and it is better than a thousand months! Every prayer, du'a, sadaqah or good act someone does is as if they've been doing it for 1000 months! That's more than 83 years - 83 years of constant 'ibadah! I'm lucky if I get 30 minutes or an hour in at a time. Just goes to show the importance of Ramadan as a whole and how much thawab we can gain. Oh Allah, please make me from those who witness the night!

I remember the hadith that I read earlier about Ramadan that said that a person who stands up in prayer on Laylat al-Qadr out of faith and seeking reward will have all his minor sins forgiven. Wow, to think that everything I have done - in one night - all gone. The imam told us a really important du'a that we should keep repeating,

اللهم انك عفو تحب العفو فاعف عنى

Allahumma innaka afuwwun tuhibbul afwa fa'fu anni

O Allah You are The One Who pardons greatly,
and loves to pardon, so pardon me.

Every time I remember that the Prophet ﷺ would stay up all night, wake up his family and work even harder in the last ten days I tell myself that I need to double my efforts. I've decided to wake up at least 2 hours before Fajr and get 2 long rak'at of Tahajjud and some du'a done.

The house is quieter now since Dad and Irfan have gone to the mosque to do *i'tikaf*. They're so lucky to be able to follow the sunnah of the Prophet ﷺ who used to practice i'tikaf in the last ten days of Ramadan till he died! His wives also used to practice i'tikaf after him. I'm feeling bad now that I didn't take the whole ten days off! Why did I only take 3 days holiday? I wonder if Michael wouldn't mind a last minute holiday booking - I doubt it. Oh well, I'll make sure I allow for the full ten days next year, insha'Allah. Anyway, the imam said that even if you couldn't do the whole 10 days of the sunnah i'tikaf, you could still sit in i'tikaf for as long as you can and you would get the reward for however long you did it. So I have decided to do i'tikaf for the weekend in my bedroom, which is where I normally pray. It's a good thing that the imam explained all the do's and don'ts of i'tikaf because this is my first time!

> **I'tikaf:** To seclude oneself with the express intention of worshipping Allah and drawing closer to Him. Men perform i'tikaf in a mosque whereas ladies can do this in a secluded part of their home.

Turn to:

• **Page 88-89** for Do's and don'ts for i'tikaf

 Ayat and Ahadith

Abu Huraira ⚘ reported that Allah's Messenger ﷺ said: "Whoever establishes the prayers on the night of Qadr out of sincere faith and hoping to attain Allah's rewards (not to show off) then all his past sins will be forgiven." (Bukhari)

We have indeed revealed this (Message) in the Night of Power:

And what will explain to thee what the night of power is?

The Night of Power is better than a thousand months.

Therein come down the angels and the Spirit by Allah's permission, on every errand:

Peace!...This until the rise of morn! (Surah Al-Qadr 97:1-5)

A'isha ⚘ reported that when the last ten nights began Allah's Messenger kept awake at night (for prayer and devotion), wakened his family, and prepared himself to observe prayer (with more vigour). (Muslim)

A'isha ⚘ reported that Allah's Messenger used to exert himself in devotion during the last ten nights to a greater extent than at any other time. (Muslim)

Day 23:

I don't usually miss days in my diary unless I'm sick or have misplaced my diary or something, but being in i'tikaf, I couldn't exactly write up my day, so I thought I'd save it till now. I cannot even begin to describe the feeling that comes even from a weekend of i'tikaf.

In fact I read an article which contained a passage from Ibn Al-Qayim's book 'Zad Al-Ma`ad' about the i'tikaf and I couldn't have put it better myself:

The basic purpose of *i'tikaf* is that the heart gets attached to Allah, and, with it, one attains inner composure and calmness; preoccupation with the mundane things of life ceases, and the state is reached in which all fears, hopes, and apprehensions are superseded by the love and remembrance of Allah; every anxiety is transformed into the anxiety for Him; every thought and feeling is blended with the eagerness to gain His nearness and to earn His good favour, and devotion to the Almighty is generated instead of devotion to the world. This is the provision for the grave where there will be neither a friend nor a helper. This is the high aim and purpose of *i'tikaf*, which is the specialty of the most sublime part of Ramadan, that is, the last ten days.

Isn't it amazing?

The Prophet ﷺ said that every day and night in Ramadan Allah frees people from Hellfire and the last ten days are known as the days of being freed from Hellfire. Oh Allah, please let me be from those whom you free from the Hellfire. Please let me be one of them. Please let me, my family, all my friends and all the Muslims be from the people you will free from the Hellfire (ameen).

 Ayat and Ahadith

A'isha ؓ reported that the Messenger of Allah ﷺ used to observe i'tikaf in the last ten days of Ramadan. (Muslim)

Ibn 'Abbas related that the Prophet ﷺ said: "Every night of Ramadan at the time of Iftar, Allah liberates a million people from the Hellfire. When Jumu'ah arrives, hourly He liberates a million people from the Hellfire, all of them deserving to be punished therein. When the last day of Ramadan comes, He liberates on that day alone, a number equal to the number that He liberated from the beginning of the month." (Ibn Rajab al-Hanbali)

Day 24:

I'm so glad I'm going to be off work in two days! It's been quite hard to maintain my routine with work and having to get up so early but I know it's all for Allah so somehow I manage to find the energy to continue, subhanallah. It's an amazing feeling to take time off work especially for Allah. I mean, how many times have I taken days off to go on holiday, but this time I'm taking it to get the most out of the last ten days and to really focus on Tahajjud and 'ibadah. I hope that Allah accepts this from me as an act of worship. It's so great how Allah can reward you on what you think are the littlest things, alhamdulillah, Allah is so merciful.

I'm also concentrating big time on saying the du'a that the imam told us about, *'Allahumma innaka afuwwun tuhibbul afwa fa'fu anni'.* That's what the Prophet ﷺ told Umm al-Mu'mineen A'isha ﷺ to say specifically on that night, so it must be important!

I've really stepped up my Qur'an reading, alhamdulillah! I'm actually 3 juz ahead now, masha'Allah. That's the beauty of i'tikaf - just having time to concentrate on reading…When I realised that I had read 5 juz over the weekend, I actually began to think of doing a second complete reading of the Qur'an! I think I'm being too ambitious really but I'll try and read as much as I can and see how it goes, with every letter accounting for ten *hasanat* and if it turns out to be Laylat al-Qadr as well then it's hasanat galore, masha'Allah! I'm not just reading though - I've really tried to focus on contemplating and understanding the words. I'm so glad I bought the Qur'an with the meanings in the margins as it's really helped my reading. Subhanallah as I read Surah az-Zumar the other day I really felt the scene of *Yawm al-Qiyamah* and the people of the Fire going into Hell and the people of the Garden going into Jannah and I just kept saying to myself, 'Please Allah let me be from the people of Jannah'. Subhanallah, that surah has always had a major effect on me.

Ok, I'd better get back to my du'a, today is the night of the 25th. Subhanallah, it might actually be tonight!

> ## 66 Ayat and Ahadith
>
> A'isha 🌸 reported that she asked Allah's Messenger 🌸: "O Messenger of Allah, if I
> know which night is Laylat al-Qadr, what should I say on that night?" He said, "Say:
> *'Allahumma innaka afuwwun tuhibbul afwa fa'fu anni';* (O Allah, You are forgiving and
> You love forgiveness, so forgive me)." (At-Tirmidhi) 99

Day 25:

Subhanallah, I just can't get over the feeling that I might not be doing
enough! There are 5 days left and that's it, Ramadan will be over – finito.
What's even worse is that there are only 2 more odd nights left! I sat and
did a quick evaluation of myself to see if there is anything I need to really
step up in the remaining days and what I haven't done. I asked Allah's
forgiveness for the times I've felt tired or a bit lazy and I'm concentrating
on thabat too.

Alhamdulillah, I'm off work tomorrow! I've decided to stay up all night
today, as the imam said that the Prophet 🌸 used to stay up all night when
the last ten days came… and not having to get up at 7 in the morning
will be a blessing! It also means I manage to get more du'a in the last third
of the night. Oh, the things I've heard about du'as at that time of night!
Imagine Allah saying to us in every last third of every night and not just in
Ramadan, *'Is there anyone supplicating to Me, so that I grant his supplication?
Is there anyone begging of Me for anything so that and I grant him his wish?'*
and I have a million things that I want from Allah. Sometimes I find myself
praying for success in my career, a bigger house and then I realise that
materialistic things like that should not be at the top of my list. Forgiveness,
oh Allah, forgiveness is what I need right now and for you to accept all my
good deeds this Ramadan, please let me be from those who are liberated
from the Hellfire, please.

I'm trying to get everyone I know to come to Taraweeh. Now that we are in the last ten days it's so much easier to get people to come as they all want to witness Laylat al-Qadr, and it means more thawab for me too! Alhamdulillah Safa and Huma have been coming to Taraweeh every night with me since the time I invited them to iftar, it's such a blessing from Allah and they really enjoy it too! Just goes to show you should never really give up on anyone!

Day 26:

Subhanallah, I know that Laylat al-Qadr is not necessarily on the night of the 27th, but still there are some opinions that say it's the 27th and the imam did the du'a for completing the Qur'an in Taraweeh today! It was so moving and the du'a had the whole mosque in tears. Not a dry eye, or nose either, in the house. And when he asked for liberation from Hellfire, I was saying to myself, 'Oh Allah, please, please make me among those who have been liberated from Hellfire.'

I might be imagining it but it's been really peaceful and everything is so quiet! Could it be? Subhanallah, it's such a blessed night, could the angels and Jibril be down on earth right now spreading Allah's mercy? Could they have been surrounding us at the mosque as the imam did the du'a and as we completed the Qur'an? I really hope so.

Well I'd better get back to praying and reading the Qur'an. I want to be one of the people whom Allah forgives their previous sins for staying up and praying during this night out of faith and in hope of earning the reward for their efforts from Him.

Day 27:

I completed my reading of the Qur'an today! All thanks to Allah for helping me finish reading the Qur'an. I called Mum, Fatima and Ali to say the du'a with me so that they can get thawab of the completion too. Imagine thousands of angels saying Ameen with us as we read the du'a! Masha'Allah that is two complete readings this Ramadan - yesterday's one at Taraweeh and my own one today! Oh Allah, please accept my readings!

I've been reading Surah al-Qadr in my prayers a lot these days to remind me of its importance. Subhanallah, the surah really stresses the honour and great value of Laylat al-Qadr and that it is of more value than 1000 months! Every time I recite it I remember its importance and it just makes me want to do so much more!

Masha'Allah, my cousin Ruqaiyyah went to 'Umrah yesterday! She is so lucky! Wow, an 'Umrah in Ramadan actually counts as a Hajj. I e-mailed her my 2 page du'a list, although I did tell her that she didn't have to say it all as I'm sure she has her own du'as to make. It's really amazing to be able to go though, I mean even seeing that massive gathering around the *Ka'bah* on TV gets me so emotional! I wonder what it's like to see the Ka'bah for real. It probably just fills you with this amazing sense of awe! I hope I can do an 'Umrah in Ramadan next year, or go on Hajj! Maybe Allah will bless me with a husband next year and we can go together, at least that would be better than waiting around for Irfan or Ali to come with me!

> **Ka'bah:** The sacred house located in al-Masjid al-Haram in Makkah

> 66   **Ayat and Ahadith**
>
> The Messenger of Allah ﷺ said: "Performing 'Umrah in the month of Ramadan equals performing Hajj." (Agreed Upon)   99

Day 28:

I had to really ask Allah for thabat and to help me continue working hard in these remaining last days. Everyone around me seems to have assumed Ramadan is already over after the night of the 27th. I can't believe that they can take such a mega risk. What if it wasn't the 27th? What if it is actually tonight?! Oh Allah, please make me from the ones who witness Laylat al-Qadr and get all my sins forgiven. The Prophet ﷺ asked us to look for it in the odd nights of the last ten nights, so it could be the 29th. Allah knows best. Anyway I am trying my hardest.

I'm also making sure I'm giving away a lot more sadaqah now so that they coincide with Laylat al-Qadr. Just to think that anything I give away would be as if I'd be doing it for 1000 months! I know I keep saying that but its thawab is so great that I just have to keep reminding myself.

It's also important not to get into any quarrels or arguments with anyone as one hadith says that the Prophet ﷺ was about to come and inform people of the date of Laylat al-Qadr but Allah made him forget it because two people were quarrelling!

Subhanallah, having the full day to concentrate on worship is brilliant! It's not just about the extra time, although that is definitely a bonus but it's also the fact that the mind is so clear and able to concentrate more instead of having to worry about the next presentation, or having to rush into a meeting or simply checking a hundred e-mails a day! I need to concentrate on doing a lot more self-reflection and trying to purify my heart. Subhanallah, getting away from material things for a bit feels good. Everything apart from Allah and worship loses its importance. I wish I could maintain that after Ramadan.

> **❝ Ayat and Ahadith**
>
> Narrated 'Ubada bin as-Samit: "The Prophet ﷺ came out to inform us about the Night of Qadr but two Muslims were quarrelling with each other. So the Prophet ﷺ said, 'I came out to inform you about the night of Qadr but such-and-such persons were quarrelling, so the news about it had been taken away, yet that might be for your own good, so seek it on the twenty-ninth and the twenty-seventh and the twenty-fifth.'" (Bukhari) ❞

Day 29:

They've just announced it! Eid is actually tomorrow! Subhanallah, I had a feeling that it might actually be tomorrow and so I concentrated on doing a lot of du'a in the last hour before Maghrib asking Allah to accept all our deeds and to forgive us for all our sins in this glorious month! I have to admit

I spent most of it crying for two reasons: 1) because I couldn't believe that it was so close to being over. I really am going to miss Ramadan so much - what am I going to do without it? It seemed as if it was only yesterday when Dad was telling us at the table, 'It will be over before you know it'. And over it is; and 2) because I really am desperate to be forgiven for all of my past sins and just hope that Allah accepts everything I've done. Oh Allah, please accept our deeds in Ramadan…wow, the Sahabah used to say this du'a for 6 months after Ramadan! 6 months! Oh Allah, please accept our deeds in Ramadan!

I just can't believe that there's no more Taraweeh! Or fasting - it just seems so strange that my Ramadan routine is all over! After 'Isha we celebrated the night of Eid and the imam said *Takbirat al Eid* a couple of times and then everyone was congratulating everyone on Eid and its arrival!

Dad and Irfan came home after their ten days in i'tikaf. I could have sworn that they had *noor* on their faces, having spent ten whole days exclusively in the pure worship of Allah. Anyway, it's good to have them home.

I must remember to speak to Dad about *Zakat al-Fitr*. He has to pay it for us as we're still a part of his household, not that it's going to rock his budget or anything, it's a very small amount per person. I must remember to say alhamdulillah for that.

Subhanallah, it really is over now…and tomorrow's Eid. It's a good thing I did my Eid shopping before Ramadan started! I really wasn't going to waste valuable time in Ramadan picking out my outfit. I've even bought new pyjamas to sleep in today! I think I picked that habit up from Mum. She's always bought all of our Eid clothes just before Ramadan starts so that she doesn't get stuck during the Holy month. Alhamdulillah for Mum!

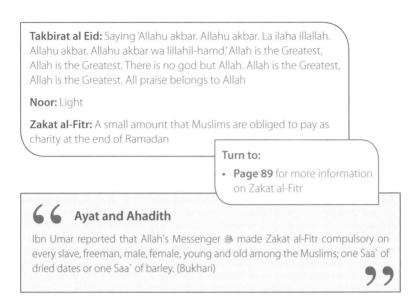

Takbirat al Eid: Saying 'Allahu akbar. Allahu akbar. La ilaha illallah. Allahu akbar. Allahu akbar wa lillahil-hamd.' Allah is the Greatest, Allah is the Greatest. There is no god but Allah. Allah is the Greatest, Allah is the Greatest. All praise belongs to Allah

Noor: Light

Zakat al-Fitr: A small amount that Muslims are obliged to pay as charity at the end of Ramadan

Turn to:
- **Page 89** for more information on Zakat al-Fitr

" " **Ayat and Ahadith**

Ibn Umar reported that Allah's Messenger ﷺ made Zakat al-Fitr compulsory on every slave, freeman, male, female, young and old among the Muslims; one Saa` of dried dates or one Saa` of barley. (Bukhari) " "

Eid!

I woke up, made ghusl, put on my new clothes and went downstairs. We all sat down as a family and had some breakfast in our best clothes! It felt so strange to get up and have something to eat!!! It felt like I was doing something wrong. The imam said that we're not allowed to fast on the first day of Eid though and everyone must break their fast. Irfan was stuffing his face with an oversized packet of crisps that he must have been saving for this special occasion.

Dad, Ali and Irfan put on some perfume and then we all walked to the mosque reciting the Eid takbirat. At least we were going back to the mosque though, maybe it wasn't for Taraweeh, but at least I saw the same faces I'd been seeing for the last month and got to hear the imam say more words of wisdom and pray behind him one last time. I think I'm going to cry again just remembering it all. I don't know why, but I always seem to cry when we say the Eid takbirat, it just sort of gets to me – I love it.

I think the imam this year was amazing. The amount of thawab that man will be getting is unbelievable. He certainly taught me a thing or two. And it didn't stop at Taraweeh nights as he encouraged us all to fast six days after Eid and within the month of *Shawwal*. He also said that if we do this, then we can get a reward equal to that as if we had been fasting for the whole year !! How amazing is Allah?? His Mercy and blessings upon us are never ending.

As with every year, the whole family went to the Eid celebration at the local mosque. All the children got gifts, food and drink was everywhere and everyone was all smiles. Fatima was so thrilled with the iPod that me and Mum got her, she was crying tears of joy.

I definitely did a lot more this Ramadan then I've probably ever done before, but I still feel that somehow I could have done some more. I think I'll start planning for next year really early, but in the meantime I will stick with what the Sahabah used to say, "Oh Allah, please accept our deeds in Ramadan" and let us live until the next and do my best to keep it up for the next 6 months.

Shawwal: The tenth month of the Islamic Calendar. The first day of Shawwal is Eid al-Fitr. There are also six days of fasting during Shawwal which, together with the Ramadan fasts, are equivalent to fasting "perpetually."

Turn to:
• **Page 90** for what is recommended on Eid day

   Ayat and Ahadith

Ibn Abbas narrated that the Prophet ﷺ offered a two rak'at prayer on the Day of Eid al-Fitr and he did not pray before or after it. Then he went towards the women along with Bilal and ordered them to pay alms and so they started giving their earrings and necklaces (in charity). (Bukhari)

Ameena's Ramadan File

RAMADAN PREPARATION PROGRAMME

6 weeks before Ramadan

'Wake up call' Week

- Recite the following *du'a* to make it to Ramadan. Do this repeatedly throughout the day and every day leading up to Ramadan:

اللهـم بارك لنا فـى رجب وشـعبان وبلـغنا رمـضان

Allahumma barik lana fi Rajab wa Sha'ban wa ballighna Ramadan

- Write down specific targets, no more than five, of things that you want to achieve this Ramadan

- Start to read books about Ramadan. This will help you get into Ramadan mode and you will also learn about the do's and don'ts of fasting, which is important if you want to derive maximum benefit from it.

5 weeks before Ramadan

'Heart Focus' Week

- Make *Tawbah Nasooha*

- Listen to Islamic lectures. Choose a scholar and topic that you feel will motivate you and get your heart into the right state

- Read Islamic books about self-development and purifying the heart

- Do your very best to pray all your *salah* on time

- Ensure that you pray the *sunnah al-mu'akkadah* rak'at with your five daily *fard* prayers

- Actively focus on improving your *khushoo'* in *salah* by spending more time on it and concentrating on what you are saying

- Allocate time to doing *tasbeeh* and *istighfar*, especially after *salah*.

4 weeks before Ramadan

'Fasting & Qur'an' Week

- Start making up the *qada* of the missed fasts from previous Ramadan(s)

- Once you have made up all your *qada* fasts, start fasting on Mondays and Thursdays

- Involve your family and friends by encouraging them to fast as well

- Allocate a certain amount of Qur'an to read every day and ensure that you read this amount regularly

- Get an English translation and a *tafsir* book to help you understand the Qur'an and read these regularly.

3 weeks before Ramadan

'Night Prayer and start thinking about charity' Week

- If one of your weak points is getting up for Fajr, now is the time to get this right by going to bed early and setting the alarm for Fajr time

- Start to pray *Qiyam ul-Layl* after 'Isha

- Start getting up for *Tahajjud*; you only need to wake up half an hour before you normally would for Fajr

- Agree with a friend or family member to wake each other up for *Tahajjud*

- Think of ways you can benefit your community and the ummah with charitable acts. Be imaginative, try and involve as many people as you can and remember that even the smallest act of kindness counts as charity.

2 weeks before Ramadan

'Increase your efforts & allocating Zakat & Sadaqah' week

- Spend more time than you already are reading and understanding the Qur'an
- Focus even more on your *salah*. You can start praying the *sunnah ghair al-mu'akkadah* and *salatul Doha*, for example
- Increase the number of rak'at you pray for *Qiyam ul-Layl* and *Tahajjud*
- Increase the amount of time you are spending on *tasbeeh* and *istighfar*
- Allocate your *zakat* if you are due to pay it
- Allocate the amount you want to pay for *sadaqah* in Ramadan and set it aside. As you do so, make an effort to read about the plight of those less fortunate than ourselves. This will have the two-fold effect of making you grateful for what you have and wanting to do more for charity.

1 week before Ramadan

'Connecting with family and friends' week

- Organise a family get together
- Contact all of your family, those who live locally as well as those abroad, to wish them the best for this Ramadan
- Organise goody bags for your family and friends' children to get them excited about Ramadan
- Take time out to sit and talk/listen to the people you live with as it can be so easy to take them for granted.

General Preparation:

- Do your Eid shopping now so as to not consume precious time during Ramadan and especially the last ten days
- Find out where you will be praying *Taraweeh*
- Print out the Ramadan check list on page 60 and put it up on your wall.

Things you will need for Ramadan:

- Qur'an with translation
- Tafsir book
- Tasbeeh/counter
- Book of *Adhkar* (e.g. Selected Prayers by Jamal Badawi)
- Abridged book of Hadith
- Lectures of a scholar that you like and a topic that motivates you
- Books that inspire you and teach you more about Islam and how to become a better Muslim
- Dates.

RAMADAN DAILY CHECKLIST

In the left column, list the things you want to do *every day* in Ramadan and then tick the boxes relevant for each of the 29/30 days of Ramadan every day

DAILY ACTIVITIES	1	2	3	4	5	6	7	8	9	10	11	12	13	14	15	16	17	18	19	20	21	22	23	24	25	26	27	28	29	30
Pray 5 fard prayers with Sunnah al-mu'akkadah																														
Pray Taraweeh																														
Read 1 juz of the Qur'an with translation																														
Spend time doing dhikr																														
Perform an act of charity																														
Eat Suhoor properly																														
Avoid swearing, lying and backbiting/gossiping																														
Lower gaze																														
Learn a hadith or ayah of the Qur'an and teach it to someone																														

Prophet Muhammad's ﷺ Khutbah on Ramadan

"O people! There comes upon you now a great and most blessed month, wherein lies a night greater in worth than a thousand months. Fasting during this month is made obligatory and extra prayers at night are optional. Whoever draws near to Allah by performing any virtuous deed in this month shall have such a reward as if he had performed an obligatory duty at any other time of the year. And whoever performs an obligatory duty shall have the reward of seventy such duties at any other time of the year."

"This is indeed the month of steadfastness (*sabr*) and the reward for true steadfastness is the Garden. It is the month of sympathy with one's fellow men. It is a month wherein a believer's livelihood is increased. Whosoever feeds a fasting person in order to break the fast at iftar will be forgiven his wrong action and freed from the Fire and he will receive a reward equal to the fasting person, without that person's reward being diminished in the least".

Some of the companions then said, "Not all of us possess the means whereby we can provide enough for a fasting person to break his fast". The Prophet ﷺ replied: "Allah grants the same reward to him who gives a fasting person a single date or a sip of milk or drink of water to break the fast."

"This is a month the first part of which brings Allah's mercy, the middle of which brings His forgiveness and the last part of which brings freedom from the Fire. Whosoever lessens the burdens of his servants in this month Allah will forgive him and free him from the Fire. And four things you should endeavour to perform in great number, two of which shall be to please your Lord while the other two shall be those without which you cannot make do. The first two qualities are to bear witness that there is no god but Allah and to ask for forgiveness. And as for the two you cannot do without: ask Allah for the Garden and seek refuge from the Fire."

"And whoever gives a fasting Muslim water to drink at iftar, Allah will grant a drink during the Day of Judgement from the fountain of Muhammad ﷺ after which he shall never again feel thirsty until he enters the Garden". (Ibn Khuzaymah, narrated by Salman al-Farsi)[1]

1. From Dr. Musharaf Hussain and Dr. Abia Afsar-Siddiqui, A Guide to Ramadan and Fasting, Ta-Ha Publishers Ltd, 2006

How to make Tawbah

TAWBAH CONSISTS OF THREE PARTS: KNOWLEDGE, REPENTANCE AND DETERMINATION

Knowledge:

If you have knowledge of Islam then you will recognise your sins and understand why they are harmful for you and know what the punishment is if you continue to do those sins. You must also have sincere faith and devotion to Allah, because if you know that something displeases/angers Him then you will feel bad about doing it.

Repentance:

Once you understand that the sins you have done are harmful and that you have earned Allah's displeasure, then you will feel bad about having sinned. You will feel deep regret and remorse, even grief at having committed those sins.

Determination:

When you feel so bad about doing those sins, then you will refrain from doing them and be determined never to do them again, especially if you know what the harmful effects and punishment are for those actions.

If you have committed a sin that involved taking away someone else's rights, then you must return those rights and ask forgiveness from that person also.[2]

---

2. Adapted from Imam al-Ghazali, Ihya Ulumuddin, translated by Maulana Fazlul Karim, Taj Company, 1982, Vol.4

TIPS TO HELP YOU STAY AWAY FROM SINS:

- Stay away from the places of sinning
- Keep yourself in the company of those who remember Allah
- Keep your hands busy with useful work and your tongue busy with remembrance of Allah
- Understand the harmful effect of sins and read about the punishment for sinning
- Remind yourself about the rewards for doing good deeds, both in this life and in the Hereafter.

Night Prayers

Any *nafl* (voluntary) prayers offered after 'Isha but before Fajr are Night Prayers. If one prays after 'Isha without going to sleep, then this prayer is called *Qiyam ul-Layl*. If one prays after waking up from sleep, then this prayer is called *Tahajjud*.

Both Qiyam ul-Layl and Tahajjud consist of a minimum of 2 rak'at with no maximum limit, which are performed in sets of two rak'at. The Prophet ﷺ used to regularly perform 8 rak'at.

There are special night prayers during Ramadan and these are called *Taraweeh*. Taraweeh is *sunnah al-mu'akkadah* which means that it is an emphasised sunnah i.e. a sunnah that the Prophet ﷺ never left. It consists of eight or twenty rak'at which are performed in sets of two rak'at. Taraweeh can be performed at home or in the mosque, but as with any other prayer, praying in congregation carries a greater reward. Three rak'at of *witr* are prayed after Salatul Taraweeh.

THE FOLLOWING MEASURES HELP IN OBSERVING NIGHT PRAYERS:

- Read up about the merits of Night Prayer. This will motivate you and make you more determined to perform it

- Just before you go to sleep, ask Allah to help you wake up for Tahajjud

- Go to bed early

- Nap during the day, if at all possible

- Avoid overeating in the evening

- Make sure that your bed is not too comfortable (otherwise you may not want to get out!).

Etiquette for Reading the Qur'an

1. You should be in a state of *taharah* (ritual purity) before you can touch the Qur'an, either by performing *ghusl* or by performing *wudu*

2. You should try to face the direction of the *Qiblah*

3. The place where you choose to sit and recite the Qur'an should be clean from any filth or bad odour

4. You should begin with *Ta'awudh*

أعـوذ بـالله مـن الشـيطان الـرجيم

'A'udhu billahi minash-shaytanir rajim

[I seek refuge from Shaytan, the cursed one], followed by

بسـم الله الرحمـن الرحيـم

Bismillahir rahman ar-rahim

[In the name of Allah, the most Kind and the most Merciful]

5. If you can read Qur'an in the Arabic language, it is preferred to recite it with the basic rules of *tajweed*

6 It is recommended to beautify your recital with a pleasant voice

7 The speed of your recitation must be regulated by your ability to understand so that you can think about what you are reading

8 If the verse contains commands and prohibitions you should immediately decide to accept or restrain from them. But if it is something you have failed to do in the past, you should seek forgiveness and intend to do it in the future. In the event that the verse contains mercy, you should feel happy and request it, or if it contains wrath, you should seek refuge in Allah. If the verse glorifies Allah, you should glorify Him

9 It is undesirable to stop reading to converse or talk to someone, laugh or play or look at something that takes away your attention, unless there is a valid reason

10 The best time to recite the Qur'an is during salah, then night-time reading, especially the latter part of it. The best time of day is after Fajr.[3]

3. Khurram Murad, Way to the Qur'an, Islamic Foundation, 1985

Draft e-mail that can be sent out to Non-Muslims

For those of you that work, you may feel the need to send out an e-mail about Ramadan in order to break the ice about the Holy month and also as a source of information and *da'wah* to your non-Muslim colleagues.

Every company has a different culture, so feel free to play about with this and tailor it to what best suits you and your work place.

Below is an example of an e-mail that has been sent around in the past from big corporate companies with over 1000 employees to small companies that have 15 members of staff.

From experience, you will find that once you have sent the e-mail, a few people will come and ask you a bit about it, so be prepared to answer their questions.

Dear All,

It's that time of year again; Ramadan is just around the corner and for those of you that don't know much about it, I've detailed some useful points below that should help give you an idea about this Holy month for Muslims.

If none of the below makes sense, or if you have any questions then please do not hesitate to ask and I will do my best to answer your questions.

Best regards,

Ameena.

*The Islamic month of Ramadan will begin on **Xth of** **20XX**
(depending on the sighting of the moon) and end on **Xrd of** **20XX**
(again depending on the sighting of the moon).*

*Some of the people you may be working with might be Muslim and
there are a few points that may be useful to know when contacting
and interacting with Muslims during this month as general life and
working patterns of Muslims change slightly during Ramadan:*

- *Fasting (Sawm) is one of the five pillars of Islam and was the
  month that the Holy Qur'an was revealed in over 1400 years ago.
  Its purpose is to provide an opportunity for Muslims to become
  more religious, increase spirituality and heavily encourages
  self-discipline.*

- *Fasting, at face value, means not consuming food or drink during
  daylight hours, for every day of the month of Ramadan, though its
  spiritual side carries much importance.*

- *Muslims are expected to fast between dawn (about an hour and a
  half before sunrise) and sunset.*

  *- During the start of Ramadan, fasting times will start and finish
  between XX:XXam and XX:XXpm approximately.*

  *- If you require a timetable, please do not hesitate to ask the
  person who has sent you this.*

- *Please be wary of these times and allow for **15 - 30 mins after
  fast breaking times** for food and prayers before contacting
  external parties or arranging meetings.*

- *The majority of Muslims will engage in Ramadan prayers
  (Taraweeh) during the evening so it may be difficult to contact them
  or expect them to be available in the evenings during this month.*

*If you have any further questions then please do not hesitate to
contact me.*

Etiquette of Making Du'a

1   In order for *du'as* to be accepted, a person should ensure that their earnings and possessions are all *halal*

2   It is recommended to face the *Qiblah* while making *du'a*

3   There are certain times and places that are more opportune for making *du'a*, such as: the Day of Arafah, during the month of Ramadan, Friday, last third of the night, at dawn, during *sajdah,* during rainfall, between *adhan* and *iqamah*, after the *fard* prayers

4   It is recommended to raise your hands to your shoulders with the palms upwards

5   It is best to begin the *du'a* with the praise of Allah and blessings upon the Prophet ﷺ

6   *Du'a* should be made with full attention and humility, in neither too loud a voice nor too quiet

7   You should not make *du'a* for anything that is *haram* or that involves harming people

8   You must be patient in having your *du'a* accepted

9   Be confident and have belief in Allah that He will accept your *du'a*

10   It is recommended to repeat your *du'a* three times

11   The best of prayers are the *du'as* of the Prophet ﷺ

12   When you make *du'a* for someone, begin by praying for yourself.[4]

4. As-Sayyid Sabiq, Fiqh us-Sunnah, American Trust Publications, 1991, Vol. IV (Funerals and Dhikr)

Du'a Sample Plan

Everyone has their own way of making *du'a*, the following plan is just to help you break it down rather than dictate what you should be saying. It helps to break down your *du'as* into categories:

1 START WITH YOURSELF AND YOUR RELIGIOUS AMBITIONS AND GOALS:

For example:

Oh Allah, please guide me to the right path and help me to become a better Muslim. Oh Allah, please help me to get the most *thawab* out of this Ramadan etc.

2 THEN FOCUS ON YOURSELF FROM A WORK OR STUDY RELATED ANGLE:

For example:

Oh Allah, please help me to achieve all my targets at work and improve the image of Muslims in my work place.

OR

Oh Allah, please help me to achieve the highest results in all of my exams this year and make studying easy for me.

3 NEXT, START MAKING DU'A FOR YOUR IMMEDIATE FAMILY (INCLUDING THOSE WHO HAVE PASSED AWAY)

For example:

Oh Allah, please guide my brother to the right path. Cure my Dad from his bad back and help make things easy for my Mum.

4 MAKE DU'A FOR THE UMMAH

For example:

Oh Allah, please make the Ummah strong and united again. Please help all of the Muslims that are suffering in all countries around the world.

5 TAKE TIME TO MAKE DU'A FOR YOUR FRIENDS AND THEIR NEEDS

For example:

Oh Allah, my friend Aisha would love to become pregnant and have a child – please grant her that wish. And Sumaiyya would love to go to Hajj this year, please make it happen, oh Allah – nothing is beyond you.

RAMADAN – THE MONTH OF FASTING
Features of good practice

✔ School has a written policy for the requirements and implications of Ramadan for their Muslim pupils

✔ School offers it's staff Ramadan awareness training about factors affecting pupils during Ramadan

✔ School recognises and celebrates the spirit and values of Ramadan through collective worship or assembly themes and communal iftar (collective breaking of the fast)

✔ School is aware of the likely increase in the number of pupils offering prayer during the month of Ramadan and facilities are provided accordingly, for example a larger area for daily prayers

✔ Adequate arrangements are in place to supervise fasting children, during the lunch hour. These arrangements are well publicised amongst pupils and parents

✔ School takes account of Ramadan when planning internal examinations and tries to avoid scheduling them during the month of Ramadan

✔ School avoids scheduling sex and relationship education and swimming during Ramadan

✔ School teachers are considerate and mindful that fasting children avoid engaging in over-demanding exercises during physical education lessons that may result in dehydration

✔ School gives the option for those Muslim pupils who are entitled to free school meals to take packed lunches home, should they wish to do so.

---

5. Muslim Council of Britain, Meeting the needs of Muslim pupils in state schools, p.32

Health Guidelines on Eating in Ramadan

AVOID:

- Fried and fatty foods. These can upset your stomach and give you indigestion and heartburn

- Foods containing too much sugar, especially at *suhoor*. These can cause your blood sugar levels to drop too quickly and can cause headaches, dizziness and tiredness

- Over-eating especially at *suhoor*. This can lead to indigestion, heartburn and constipation

- Too much tea at *suhoor:* Tea makes you pass more urine taking with it valuable mineral salts that your body would need during the day.

EAT:

- Slow-digesting foods at *suhoor*. These last longer in the body thus making you feel less hungry

- Dates are excellent source of sugar, fibre, carbohydrates, potassium and magnesium

- Almonds are rich in protein and fibre with less fat

- Bananas are a good source of potassium, magnesium and carbohydrates.

DRINK:

- As much water or fruit juices as possible between *iftar* and bedtime so that your body can adjust fluid levels in time.

The Three Levels of Fasting in Ramadan

IMAM AL-GHAZALI WRITES ABOUT THE FOLLOWING CATEGORIES OF FASTING:

First level: Ordinary Fasting

This level requires abstention from three things: food, drink and sexual satisfaction. This is the minimum requirement and the reward is given accordingly.

Second level: Special Fasting

Keeping one's ears, eyes, tongue, hands and feet free from sin. For such people just abstaining from the minimum requirement is not sufficient, thus they take care not to say, hear or do a wrong thing. As they restrain their organs from all kinds of prohibitions, they are rewarded accordingly.

Third level: Extra-special Fasting

This fast involves abstaining from all unworthy thoughts, loves, desires and wishes in total disregard of everything except the thought and remembrance of Allah. This is the perfection of *tawhid* (oneness of Allah). One may physically be present in the world but the internal self is exclusively engaged towards Allah.[6]

Etiquette of Friday

1   Make preparations for Friday from 'Asr time on Thursday by doing *istighfar* and *tasbeeh*. Ensure that your clean clothes are ready so that this does not take up valuable time on Friday morning. Read Qur'an and extra prayers on Thursday night

2   Perform *ghusl* on Friday morning. It is best to clip the nails, cleanse the teeth and do everything necessary to be in a state of ritual purity

3   It is desirable to recite Surah al-Kahf on Friday

4   Spend plenty of time in prayer throughout the day, as there is a time in which *du'as* are accepted on this day

5   Send salat and salaam on the Prophet ﷺ

6   It is recommended to give charity on this day as the rewards are increased

7   It is recommended to minimise worldly affairs and concentrate on *'ibadah*.[7]

6 & 7. Adapted from Imam al-Ghazali, Ihya Ulumuddin, translated by Maulana Fazlul Karim, Taj Company, 1982, Vol.1

Daily Prayer

THE DAILY PRAYERS ARE AS FOLLOWS:

Fajr (Subh) (Dawn Prayer):

Two rak'at of *sunnah al-mu'akkadah* followed by two rak'at of *fard*.

Dhuhr (Noon Prayer):

Four rak'at of *sunnah al-mu'akkadah*, four rak'at of *fard* followed by two rak'at of *sunnah al-mu'akkadah*.

'Asr (Afternoon Prayer):

Four rak'at of *sunnah ghair al-mu'akkadah* followed by four rak'at of *fard*. Note that it is forbidden to perform sunnah prayers after 'Asr until sunset.

Maghrib (Sunset Prayer):

Three rak'at of *fard* followed by two rak'at of *sunnah al-mu'akkadah*.

'Isha (Night Prayer):

Four rak'at of *sunnah ghair al-mu'akkadah*, four rak'at of *fard* and two rak'at of *sunnah al-mu'akkadah*.

Witr:

This comprises three rak'at. Witr can be performed immediately after the two rak'at sunnah of 'Isha, or it can be performed just before sleeping, or after Tahajjud.

Nafl:

(Voluntary) prayers can be performed with any of the five daily prayers in sets of two rak'at apart from the time after Asr until sunset and after Fajr until sunrise.

Salatul Doha:

This is a *nafl* prayer, which can be performed from after sunrise to before Dhuhr time. It consists of between two and twelve rak'at, performed in sets of two rak'at.

NOTE:

- *Fard* prayers are obligatory and neglecting these makes a person a sinner

- *Sunnah al-mu'akkadah* prayers are an emphasised sunnah i.e. the Prophet ﷺ never neglected to perform these

- *Sunnah ghair al-mu'akkadah* prayers carry a reward if performed but no punishment if not performed

- *Nafl* prayers bring extra reward if performed.

Reflection and Contemplation: Some active help

Have you ever thought about the fact that you did not exist before you were conceived and then born into the world and that you have come into existence from mere nothingness?

Have you ever thought about how the fragrant and beautifully coloured flowers you see everyday have come out of pitch black, muddy soil?

Have you ever thought about how mosquitoes, which irritatingly fly around you, move their wings so fast that we are unable to see them?

Have you ever thought about how the peels of fruits such as bananas, watermelons, melons and oranges serve as wrappings of high quality, and how the fruits are packed in these wrappings so that they maintain their taste and fragrance?

Have you ever thought about the possibility that while you are asleep a sudden earthquake could raze your home, your office, and your city to the ground and that in a few seconds you could lose everything of the world you possess?

Have you ever thought of how your life passes away very quickly, and that you will grow old and become weak, and slowly lose your beauty, health and strength?

Have you ever thought about how one day you will find the angels of death appointed by Allah before you and that you will then leave this world?

Have you ever thought about why people are so attached to a world from which they will soon depart when what they basically need is to strive for the Hereafter?

Man is a being whom Allah furnishes with the faculty of thought. Yet, most people do not use this very important faculty as they should. In fact, some people almost never think.

In truth, each person possesses a capacity for thought of which even he himself is unaware. Once man begins to use this capacity, facts he has not been able to realise until that very moment begin to be uncovered for him. The deeper he goes in reflection, the more his capacity to think improves, and this is possible for everyone. One just has to realise that one needs to reflect and then to strive hard.[8]

8. Harun Yahya, Deep Thinking, Ta-Ha Publishers Ltd., 2000

Things you can do when you are menstruating

1. Read a translation of the Qur'an or a *tafsir* book

2. Make *du'a* and spend time engaging in *dhikr*

3. Listen to the Qur'an or recite from memory

4. Read Islamic books

5. Attend religious classes (although not those that take place in the actual prayer area of the mosque)

6. Increase your *da'wah* activities

7. Give charity and think of ways of encouraging others to give charity

8. Help around at home with the intention of gaining *thawab*

9. Offer to help out with taking care of children at the mosque while others pray

10. Offer to baby-sit for someone who has children and may want to go to Taraweeh

11. Try to find out about Islamic activities going on in your local area and try and get involved with organising them

12. Try and feed as many fasting people as you can – go to places that organise mass *iftars* and offer to help or give *sadaqah* towards it.

Remember it is your intention that matters!

Dhikr and Remembrance of Allah[9]

'Ali ibn Abi Talha relates that Ibn Abbas said, "All obligations imposed upon man by Allah are clearly marked and one is exempted from them in the presence of a genuine cause. The only exception is the obligation of *dhikr*. Allah has set no specific limits for it, and under no circumstances is one allowed to be negligent of it. We are commanded to 'remember Allah standing, sitting and reclining on your sides' (3:191), in the morning, during the day, at sea or on land, on a journey or at home, in poverty and in prosperity, in sickness or in health, openly and secretly, and in fact at all times throughout one's life and in all circumstances."

"Verily in the remembrance of Allah do hearts find peace" (13:28)

"Those men and women who engage much in Allah's praise. For them Allah has prepared forgiveness and a great reward." (33:35)

Excellence of saying

لَا إِلَهَ إِلَّا اللّٰهُ   *La ilaha ill-Allah*

Jabir ⬥ reported that the Prophet ⬥ said, "The best remembrance of Allah is to repeat *La ilaha illallah* and the best prayer is *alhamdulillah*." (An-Nasa'i, Ibn Majah and Al-Hakim)

Excellence of *Tasbih, Hamd, Tahlil, Takbir* and others

Abu Huraira ⬥ reported that the Prophet ⬥ said, "There are two phrases that are light on the tongue but heavy on the scale of rewards and are dear to Allah. These are: *Subhanallah wa bihamdihi* (All glory is to Allah and all praise to Him) and *Subhanallah al-Azim* (Glorified is Allah the Great)." (Muslim, Bukhari and At-Tirmidhi)

Samura ibn Jundab ⬥ reported that the Prophet ⬥ said, "The dearest phrases to Allah are four: *Subhanallah* (Glorified is Allah), *alhamdulillah*

---

9. As-Sayyid Sabiq, Fiqh us-Sunnah, American Trust Publications, 1991, vol. IV (Funerals and Dhikr)

(all praise is due to Allah), *la ilaha illallah* (there is no god but Allah), *Allahu akbar* (Allah is the Greatest)

سـبـحـان اللّه , لا الـه الا اللّه اللّه أكـبـر

There is no harm in beginning them in any order you choose while remembering Allah." (Muslim)

Abu Sa'id 🙵 reported that the Prophet 🙵 said, "Perform the enduring deeds more frequently." They asked, "What are these enduring deeds?" The Prophet 🙵 replied, "*At-Takbir, At-Tahlil, At-Tasbih, alhamdulillah* and

لا حـول ولا قـوة الا بـاللّه

la hawla wala quwwata illa billah [There is no power nor any might except with the permission of Allah]." (An-Nasa'i and Al-Hakim)

(*Takbir* means saying *Allahu Akbar, Tahlil* means saying *la ilaha illallah, Tasbih* means saying *subhanallah*)

Excellence of Istighfar

Abdallah ibn Abbas 🙵 said, "If one supplicates without fail for forgiveness from Allah, He finds a way out for him to get out of every distress and difficulty, and gives him sustenance through ways utterly unthought of." (Abu Dawud, An-Nasai, Ibn Majah, Al-Hakim)

Merits of reciting Subhanallah

Juwairiya 🙵 reported that Allah's Messenger 🙵 came out from (her apartment) in the morning as she was busy in observing her dawn prayer in her place of worship. He came back in the forenoon and she was still sitting there. He (the Holy Prophet) said to her: 'You have been in the same seat since I left you.' She said: 'Yes.' Thereupon Allah's Apostle 🙵 said: 'I recited four words three times after I left you and if these are to be weighed against what you have recited since morning these would outweigh them and (these words) are *Subhanallah wa bihamdihi 'adada khalqihi wa rida' nafsihi wa zinata 'arshihi wa midada kalimatihi* [Hallowed be Allah and praise is due to Him according to the number of His creation and according to the pleasure of His Self and according to the weight of His Throne and according to the ink (used in recording) words (for His Praise)].' (Muslim and Abu Dawud)

Valid Reasons for Forgoing a Fast

SOME OF THESE EXEMPTIONS ARE OPTIONAL.

- Children under the age of puberty (Young children are encouraged to fast as much as they are able)
- People who are mentally incapacitated or not responsible for their actions
- The elderly
- The sick
- Travellers who are on journeys of more than about fifty miles
- Pregnant women and nursing mothers
- Women who are menstruating

Those who are temporarily unable to fast must make up the missed days at another time or feed the poor.

Suggested Activities for the Last Ten Days of Ramadan

1   Make a big effort to increase all your religious activities for the last ten days, such as extra prayers and more *dhikr*

2   Keep reciting this special *du'a*:

اللهم انك عفو تحب العفو فاعف عنى

Allahumma innaka 'afuwwun tuhibbu'l-'afwa fa'fu 'anni

Oh Allah, You are indeed pardoning and You love to pardon, so pardon me

3   Make *tawbah*

4   Evaluate yourself and see how you could be a better person

5   Make long, sincere and deep *du'as*

6   Spend quality time with your family

7   Try to finish the Qur'an and read the *du'a* for the completion of Qur'an recitation

8   Spend some time in *i'tikaf*. If you cannot fulfil the sunnah of sitting in *i'tikaf* for 10 days then you can sit in seclusion for any length of time with the sole purpose of drawing closer to Allah and you will, insha'Allah, be rewarded accordingly

9   Try to minimise the time you spend on worldly matters. You could try not watching TV, listening to music or surfing the internet for this short period of time and this will all help you in drawing closer to Allah

10   Try to memorise some of the shorter surahs in the 30th juz which you can recite in your *salah*

11   Read and learn some hadith and try to practice these in your daily life.

I'tikaf

I'tikaf is when a person stays in the mosque with the sole intention of worshipping Allah and drawing closer to Him, while turning his attention away from worldly affairs as much as possible. Women can do *i'tikaf* at home in a secluded area of the house where they usually pray.

The retreat of the last ten days of Ramadan is a *sunnah al-mu'akkadah 'ala kifayah*, which means that it is *sunnah al-mu'akkadah* upon the community. If at least one person from a locality sits in *i'tikaf* for this time, then the whole community is absolved of this responsibility. Sunnah *i'tikaf* starts at Maghrib of the 20th day and ends upon the announcement of Eid.

If someone is unable to sit in *i'tikaf* for the whole ten day period, then they can also perform *i'tikaf*, but this would be a *mustahabb* or *nafl i'tikaf*. This can be performed for any length of time and the reward is given accordingly.

The time in *i'tikaf* must be spent doing *salah*, *dhikr*, reading the Qur'an, making *du'a*, reading religious books, making *tawbah* and sending salutations on the Prophet ﷺ.

Permissible acts

1) The person may go out at any time for some need that he must perform such as answering the call of nature, doing *wudu* or *ghusl*

2) It is permissible to leave the mosque to eat and drink if food and drink are not made available in the mosque

Actions that Nullify the I'tikaf

1) Intentionally leaving the mosque even if it is for just a short time (in the case of the *sunnah i'tikaf*)

2) State of menstruation or post-childbirth bleeding.

Zakat al-Fitr

Zakat al-Fitr becomes obligatory on every Muslim, male or female, adult or child, at the end of Ramadan as long as he/she has the means to do so, even those who have not fasted during the month of Ramadan for any valid reason.

Ibn Abbas ؓ reported that the Prophet ﷺ made *zakat al-Fitr* compulsory so that those who fasted may be purified of their idle deeds and shameful talk (committed during Ramadan) and so that the poor may be fed. Whoever gives it before *salah* will have it accepted as *zakah*, while he who gives it after the *salah* has given *sadaqah*. (Abu Dawud)

Therefore, *zakat al-Fitr* is to provide those who fasted with the means of making up for their errors during the month of fasting, just as any sadaqah washed away sins. *Zakat al-Fitr* also provides the poor with the means with which they can celebrate Eid al-Fitr along with the rest of the Muslims.

As mentioned in the above hadith it should be given before the Eid prayer so that it can be distributed to the poor in time for the Eid celebrations, so that they may participate also.

The local mosque will advise as to the rate of *zakat al-Fitr* that should be given. The head of the household is responsible for the payment of himself and his dependants.

The Sunnah of Eid

- To wake up early, in order to prepare for the sunnahs of the day

- To perform *ghusl*

- Apply perfume (men only)

- Wear the best clothes available to you (without excess)

- Eat before going for Eid prayer. The sunnah is to eat an odd number of dates

- To walk to the place of prayer, if at all possible, reciting the *takbirat*, which is

الله اكبر الله اكبر لا اله الا الله الله اكبر الله
اكبر ولله الحمد

*Allahu Akbar, Allahu Akbar, la ilaha illallah. Allahu Akbar,
Allahu akbar wa lillahil hamd*

Allah is the Greatest, Allah is the Greatest. There is no god but Allah.
Allah is the Greatest, Allah is the Greatest. All praise belongs to Allah.

- To return from the place of prayer using a different route to the one taken to get there.

Glossary

Adhkar: Specific du'a to be said in different situations

Ahadith (plural of hadith): Narration of the sayings and deeds of the Prophet Muhammad ﷺ

Astaghfirullah: I ask Allah for His forgiveness

Ayat (plural of ayah): Verses of the Qur'an

Da'wah: Calling to or inviting others to Islam or acts of worship or general good

Doha Prayer: A nafl daytime prayer

Du'a: Supplication to Allah

Ghusl: Full ablution (ritual washing)

Hajj: The fifth pillar of Islam, the major pilgrimage to Makkah

Halal: Allowed/permissible in Islam

Haram: Forbidden in Islam

Hasanat: Rewards

'Ibadah: Worship

Iftar: The evening meal for breaking the daily fast

Istighfar: Seeking forgiveness from Allah by saying Astaghfirullah (I seek forgiveness from Allah)

I'tikaf: To seclude oneself with the express intention of worshipping Allah and drawing closer to Him. Men perform i'tikaf in a mosque whereas ladies can do this in a secluded part of their home

Ka'bah: The sacred house located in al-Masjid al-Haram in Makkah

Khushoo': Humbleness and submission of the heart and mind with concentration in worship

Khutbah: Islamic sermon or speech

La Hawla Wala Quwwata Illa Billah: There is no might and no power except with Allah

Niyyah: Intention

Laylat al-Qadr: The Night of Decree

Maghfirah: Forgiveness

Noor: Light

Qada: The making up of fasts missed for a valid reason during the previous Ramadan

Qiyam: Nafl (voluntary) Night time prayer

Rizq: Sustenance, provision

Sahabah: Companions of the Prophet Muhammad ﷺ

Sajdah: The act of prostration

Salah: Prayer, particularly the five daily obligatory prayers which are the second pillar of Islam

Salat alar-Rasool: Praying upon the Prophet ﷺ

Rahmah: Mercy

Sadaqah: Charity in its various forms

Silat ar-Rahm: Maintaining the ties of the womb (relations), visiting family and keeping in touch with them

Shawwal: The tenth month of the Islamic calendar. The first day of Shawwal is Eid al-Fitr. There are also six days of fasting during Shawwal which, together with the Ramadan fasts, are equivalent to fasting "perpetually"

Shayateen (plural of Shaytan): Devils

Suhoor: The meal consumed early in the morning before Fajr

Sunnah: The way of the Prophet ﷺ. They are the physical actions and sayings that were instituted by Prophet Muhammad ﷺ that we should follow in our daily lives

Sunnah Prayers: Ritual prayers that the Prophet ﷺ performed in addition to the fard (obligatory) prayers

Tafsir: Qur'anic commentary

Tahajjud: Nafl (voluntary) night time prayer

Takbirat al Eid: Saying 'Allahu akbar. Allahu akbar. La ilaha illallah. Allahu akbar. Allahu akbar wa lillahil-hamd.' Allah is the Greatest, Allah is the Greatest. There is no god but Allah. Allah is the Greatest, Allah is the Greatest. All praise belongs to Allah

Taraweeh: Night prayers during Ramadan

Tasbeeh: Glorifying or praising Allah such as saying Allahu Akbar (Allah is Great), Alhamdulillah (All praise to Allah), and Subhanallah (Glory to Allah)

Tawbah nasooha: A real repentance, asking Allah's forgiveness for one's sins and intending never to repeat them again

Thabat: Continuing on the straight path, steadfastness

Thawab: Reward

'Umrah: The 'lesser pilgrimage' that can be undertaken at any time of year

Yawm al-Qiyamah: The Day of Judgement

Zakat: The third pillar of Islam, this is the spending of a fixed portion of one's wealth for the poor or less fortunate

Zakat al-Fitr: A small amount that Muslims are obliged to pay as charity at the end of Ramadan

Your Ramadan Notes

Your Ramadan Notes

Your Ramadan Notes